Marlin Av

Mathematical Theory of Elementary Particles

Proceedings
of the
Conference
on the

Mathematical Theory of Elementary Particles

held at
Endicott House,
in Dedham, Massachusetts,
September 12–15, 1965

Edited by
Roe Goodman
and
Irving Segal

The M.I.T. Press
Massachusetts Institute of Technology
Cambridge, Massachusetts, and London, England

Library of Congress Catalog Card Number: 66-27212

Printed in the United States of America

FOREWORD

This book represents the relatively formal part of the program at the international Conference on the Mathematical Theory of Elementary Particles held in September, 1965, at M.I.T.'s Endicott House. The aim of the Conference was partly to emulate the success of the earlier Conference on Analysis in Function Space in helping to overcome serious problems of communication and cooperation between scientists concerned with different phases of a highly active interdisciplinary development, as well as to continue in a broader context some of the scientific dialogues developed at the earlier Conference. In comparable measure, it was motivated by the observation that the rigorous mathematical approach to elementary particles had come of age.

A quite broad spectrum of mathematical approaches to elementary particle theory was represented by the mathematicians and physicists in attendance at the Conference. There were in particular mathematicians concerned with most of the basically relevant mathematical fields; quantum field theorists of both axiomatic and constructivist persuasions (some of whom have legs in both outposts); and group-theoretical single-particleers. It is impossible to recapture the many discussions and informal seminars that were a crucial part of the Conference. The present Proceedings is possibly as representative as a formal report can be: it includes the invited opening survey, invited addresses, and a number of seminars on quite recent work. Roughly half of the text represents work whose level of rigor is that of contemporary mathematics; the other half, dealing in part with approximate or intuitive matters, represents a comparatively very high level of scientific precision, in our view. We hope that this volume has sufficient breadth, topicality, and elementary clarity to be useful for orientation purposes, as well as of interest to experts in the subject of the Conference.

Financial support for the Conference was provided by the Office of Scientific Research of the United States Air Force. Its scientific planning was the work of a Committee consisting of the present editors together with Sidney Coleman, Mark Kac, Gunnar Källén, George W. Mackey, Robert G. Pohrer, and Steven Smale. One of the editors (I. S.) feels called upon to record the vital contribution made by the other (R. G.) in his capacity as Executive Secretary for the Conference.

Cambridge, Mass.
February, 1966

Roe Goodman
Irving Segal

CONTENTS

Mathematical Theory of Elementary Particles

Chapter 1

SEVEN TYPES OF U(6)*

Sidney Coleman

Let us put a little order in these revels; measure is required even in the depths of infamy and delirium.

D. A. F. de Sade: La Philosophie dans le boudoir

This lecture is not properly about physics at all; it is about nosonomy, the classification of diseases. In particular, it is about the attempts made to construct a relativistic U(6) theory after Sakita, Gürsey, and Radicati exploded their bombshell last August. I suppose it is best to begin with a few warnings:

1. I am concerned here with the structure of theories rather than their predictions. If you want Clebsch-Gordon coefficients and comparisons with experiment, you will have to go elsewhere. This distorts in some measure the appearance of this chronicle, by omitting the motivation for most of the theory-building described.

2. This talk is organized in quasi-historical order. By this I mean that I have arranged theories in types, in such a way that it might seem to a naive listener that each type was invented and explored, its difficulties discovered, and the next type invented in an attempt to overcome these difficulties. This is, of course, a gross distortion: in reality, many of these theories were pro-

*This paper is based on two talks, one given at the Endicott House Conference on the Mathematical Theory of Elementary Particles, September, 1965, and one given at the East Coast Theoretical Physics Conference, November, 1965.

posed at the same time (sometimes even in the same paper). I think the gain in clarity makes this sort of arrangement preferable to a strict historical narrative.

3. I have been Procrustean in fitting some theories into my neat framework. This is especially true of the theories of the sixth type; the assumptions I state are quite different in form from those proposed in the original papers. However, to the best of my knowledge, they are equivalent, and yield the same results.

4. There are some comments at the end about promising recent developments. These are even more incoherent than the rest of the talk; live theories are notoriously more resistant to analysis than dead ones.

Type One: Nonrelativistic U(6)

The first U(6) theories were proposed independently by Sakita and by Gürsey and Radicati. These theories were all based on a model in which the observed "elementary" particles were considered as bound states of quarks, hypothetical spin-one-half unitary triplets. The forces between quarks must be invariant under U(3), in order to reproduce the observed symmetry of the strong interactions. However, at least in the nonrelativistic limit, it is possible to go much further than this: it is easy to write down interactions that are not only independent of the orientation of the quarks in unitary-spin space, but also of their orientation in ordinary spin-space. The strong interactions are then invariant under a group that shuffles all six quark degrees of freedom; this group is isomorphic to U(6), and the multiquark bound states therefore belong to irreducible representations of this grou (A similar phenomenon, with U(4) replacing U(6), occurs in Wigner's supermultiplet theory of nuclear structure.)

For example, in the original Gürsey-Radicati paper, the octet of baryons and the decuplet of baryon resonances were placed in a 56-dimensional representation of the group ($8 \times 2 + 10 \times 4 = 56$) while the octet of pseudoscalar mesons and the nonet of vector mesons were place in a 35-dimensional representation ($8 \times 1 + 9 \times 3 = 35$).

This hypothesis — U(6) invariance of the strong interactions — represented a completely new departure in particle physics. Previously we had only dealt with purely internal symmetries (e.g., U(3)), or purely geometrical ones (e.g., the Poincaré group). Only nine of the generators of U(6) are of the first type, and only three of the second. The other 24 generators are objects of mixed character; for example, they turn a neutron spinning up into a proton spinning down. It is, of course, precisely the presence of these generators which enables us to place particles of different spin in a single representation of the group.

Nonrelativistic U(6) had many successes. Beyond the classification of the hadrons, perhaps the most striking was the prediction of the magnetic moment ratio of the neutron and proton,

$$\frac{\mu_n}{\mu_p} = -\frac{3}{2},$$

derived from the symmetry group and the assumption that the magnetic-moment operator transformed like a component of a 35. However, the theory was not without its difficulties. In the first place, there were difficulties of principle: The theory was firmly based on the separation of spin and orbital angular momentum; this separation is inherently nonrelativistic, and thus the theory is also (at least in appearance). In the second place, there were difficulties of practice: The three spin generators are in the algebra of U(6), so spin and orbital angular momentum are independently conserved. Thus such popular processes as these are forbidden:

$$\rho \not\rightarrow 2\pi$$

$$N^* \not\rightarrow N + \pi$$

$$N \not\rightarrow N + \pi$$

(The first two are forbidden by spin conservation alone; the last requires parity invariance in addition.)

These difficulties are evidently closely connected; if a proper relativistic generalization were to be found, it would ineluctably mix up spin and orbital angular momentum and, thus, hopefully, allow the previously forbidden processes.

The rest of this paper deals with attempts to construct such generalizations.

Second Type: Naive Relativistic U(6)

This type of theory attempts to generalize the nonrelativistic theory in the most naive way; the relativistic theory is supposed to be invariant under a symmetry group that combines the Poincaré group and U(3) in the same way in which the symmetry group of the nonrelativistic theory combines the Galileo group and U(3). To be precise: We assume there is a Lie group G, represented by unitary transformations on the underlying Hilbert space of the system, which contains the Poincaré group and U(3), and which is not simply a direct product of these groups.

It is easy to find groups with the required structure. I will explicitly construct two examples.

1. Let U(6, 6) be the group of all linear transformations on complex 12-vectors which leaves invariant the quadratic form

$$\sum_{i=1}^{6} z_i^* z_i - \sum_{i=7}^{12} z_i^* z_i .$$

We may think of U(6, 6) as the group of all transformations on a set of three Dirac bispinors which leaves invariant the form

$$\sum_{i=1}^{3} \overline{\psi}^i \psi^i .$$

From this definition it is clear that U(6, 6) contains both an image of U(3) and an image of the homogeneous Lorentz group. Let P' be a group isomorphic to the Poincaré group. Then the symmetry group of the theory is taken to be

$$G \cong U(6,6) \otimes P'.$$

A general element of this group may be written as (g, Λ, a), where g is an element of U(6, 6), Λ is homogeneous Lorentz transformation, and a is a translation. The actual Poincaré group P is identified with the set of all elements of the form (Λ, Λ, a). The physical idea is this: Just as rotations, in the nonrelativistic theory, are divided into space and spin parts, so the same is done here with Lorentz transformations. The total Lorentz transformation is effected by simultaneously performing a "space" transformation and a "spin" transformation.

2. Here also we use U(6, 6), but we imbed it in a larger group in a different way. The group U(6, 6) has a 143-dimensional real representation; therefore we may consider it as a group of automorphisms on a 143-parameter Abelian group. The symmetry group G is the semidirect product of U(6, 6) with such a group. This contains the Poincaré group in an obvious way. In contrast to our first example, the entire Lorentz group is now inside U(6, 6); however, we now have 139 extra "translation" operators.

It is clear that these methods may be extended to any semi-simple group which contains the direct product of SU(3) and the homogeneous Lorentz group. However, the only other group to be widely exploited in the literature is the group of all unimodular transformations on six complex variables SL(6, C).

Now that we have our groups, we would like to examine some properties of the worlds in which they are exact symmetries of the fundamental interactions. In particular, we would like to find the irreducible unitary representations of G, for the one-particle states must transform like a basis for a sum of these; thus knowledge of these tells us the possible hadron supermultiplets.

Let us begin with our first example, $U(6, 6) \otimes P'$. The necessary analysis is a trivial extension of the classic work of Wigner on the Poincaré group. Let P_μ be the four generators of space translations. Then

$$m^2 = P_\mu P^\mu$$

commutes with all the generators of the group and is a constant for all the irreducible representations. Thus, all the particles in a supermultiplet have the same mass. We are, of course, particularly interested in the cases where m^2 is greater than or equal to zero. Let us consider the first case. The P_μ all commute and may therefore all be simultaneously diagonalized. In any irreducible representation all momentum four-vectors on the mass hyperboloid must occur. Let us consider those states for which P_μ has the value (m, 0, 0, 0), and let us define the little group of G as that subgroup which leaves this set invariant. Then, as Wigner has shown, the irreducible unitary representations of G are characterized by the irreducible unitary representations of the little group.

In our case, the little group is $U(6, 6) \otimes SO(3)$. Now U(6, 6) is noncompact; furthermore, it has no local compact factor groups. Thus, all the nontrivial representations of U(6, 6) are infinite-dimensional, and there are an infinite number of particles in every supermultiplet — a catastrophic result.

We may apply the same analysis to our second example. Here we begin by diagonalizing the 143 translationlike generators. Just as before, all values of the momentum 143-vector lying on an invariant surface must occur. But this is already disastrous! For it is easy to see that this implies that the physical mass — the sum of the squares of only four components of the momentum — must run through a continuum of values.

Once again we have an infinite number of particles in a supermultiplet, although in this case it is a mass continuum rather than degenerate "spin infinity."

A useful concept in discussing this phenomenon is that of "particle finiteness." A group G, containing the Poincaré group P, is said to be particle-finite if it possesses at least one locally faithful unitary representation with the property that, if G is restricted to P, the representation decomposes into a direct sum of a finite number of irreducible positive-mass representations of P. If a group is not particle-finite, it is said to be particle-infinite.

In this language, the trouble with the groups we have been discussing is that they are particle-infinite. There is a conjecture that every particle finite group is essentially locally isomorphic to a direct product of P and a compact Lie group. (For a precise definition of "essentially" see my paper, listed in the bibliography.) This conjecture has been proved for a wide class of Lie groups, but not for all. First unsolved problem for mathematicians: Either prove the conjecture for all Lie groups, or find a counterexample.

If the conjecture is true, any attempt to construct a relativistic U(6) theory of the second type is doomed to failure.

The Next Two Types

The next two types of theories may be thought of as alternative attempts to avoid the difficulties of type two theories. On the one hand, we may try and live with particle-infinite theories. After all, it is not at all implausible to assume that there are an infinite number of strongly interacting resonances, strung out along the energy spectrum, and it might be of interest to consider the approximation in which all these resonances are degenerate. This would certainly be a very bad approximation for mass spectra, but it might be a reasonable one for computing coupling constants. (We have some reason for optimism in the example of U(3), where quite large mass splittings do not seem to have large effects on vertex functions.) Something like the situation envisaged here occurs in the strong-coupling model of the nucleon, where there are an infinite series of excited states, all of which become degenerate when the coupling becomes infinitely strong.

On the other hand, we may turn to more general objects than Lie groups, for example, infinite-parameter groups. The conjecture of the preceding section is certainly not true in this case. For example, if we consider the group of all unitary transformations on the states of a single spinless particle, this group is certainly particle-finite, contains the Poincare group, and is not a direct product.

Type Three: Particle-Infinite Theories

This type of theory has been investigated by Budini and Fronsdal and also by Zumino and Wess. Curiously enough, in this case it is even possible to build a field theory that displays the desired symmetry. (At least for bosons; there are some technical difficulties in the fermion case.) For definiteness, let us consider the group U(6, 6) $\otimes$ P', already discussed. Let $\phi^{\alpha}(x)$ be an infinite set of fields, such that the factor U(6, 6) acts only on the index α, transforming it according to some infinite-dimensional unitary representation of the group, and the factor P' acts only on the space variable x, transforming it in the usual way. Then the Lagrangian density

$$\sum_\alpha \partial^\mu \phi^{\alpha *} \partial_\mu \phi^\alpha + g\left(\sum_\alpha \phi^{\alpha *}\phi^\alpha\right)^2$$

describes a theory which is invariant under the action of the group, and which seems to be as consistent as the usual field theories involving only a finite number of fields.

Thus this type of theory will never encounter any difficulties in principle; it may, however, encounter difficulties in practice: the predictions may be bad. This seems to be the unfortunate case for all theories of this kind so far investigated. To take one example: We would like to preserve the idea of vector-meson dominance of electromagnetic form factors. This is impossible. The vector mesons must belong to an infinite-dimensional unitary representation of the group; however, the form factors at zero momentum-transfer transform according to a finite-dimensional, nonunitary representation (the adjoint representation). Thus it is impossible for there to be a linear relation between these two entities (Schur's Lemma!). There are also severe problems in constructing an invariant meson-baryon coupling, but I do not have the time to discuss these here.

Since there is no difficulty of principle, it is still possible that a satisfactory theory might be constructed along these lines. All that can be said is that, at the present time, this has not been done.

Fourth Type: Infinite-Parameter Groups

Theories of this type have been considered by Gürsey, Mahanthappa and Sudarshan, and others. Here the groups are usually chosen so that they are invariances of a system of free quarks; thus the particle-infinity difficulty cannot arise. However, a new difficulty appears in its place: the only invariant S-matrix is the trivial one, S = 1.

Very roughly, the reason for this is that with an infinite-parameter group, one has an infinite number of conserved commuting quantum numbers. Conservation of all of these quantities restricts the S-matrix to such an extent that no scattering is possible. It is not known whether this difficulty is general or simply a special feature of the groups that have been investigated. I suspect the former is the case, but I have been unable to construct a proof. Second unsolved problem for mathematicians: Either prove the difficulty is general or find a counterexample.

Fifth Type: Intrinsically Broken Symmetries

I will speak very briefly about this class of theories, which has been investigated by many authors. (See the Bibliography.) The fundamental observation is that it is easy to construct an interaction Lagrangian that is invariant under (for example) U(6, 6) ⊗ P'. Here is an example, using quark fields

$$\mathscr{L}' = (\overline{\psi}\psi)^2.$$

(The sum over unitary-spin indices is implied.) The free Lagrangian,

$$\mathscr{L}_0 = \overline{\psi}(\gamma_\mu \partial^\mu - m)\psi,$$

however, couples space and spin and breaks the symmetry. The hope is that in some strong-coupling limit the interaction Lagrangian will dominate the free Lagrangian, and its symmetries will become approximate symmetries of the theory.

But if this hope is fullfilled, we would be brought back to the difficulties of the theories of the second type! Thus there is no advantage to this approach.

However, in the current state of our knowledge of field theory, there is no reason to believe that the hope should be fulfilled; as far as we know, the proposition that the interaction Lagrangian possesses symmetries not shared by the free Lagrangian is without observable consequences, either desirable or undesirable.

(In fairness to the authors so cavalierly dismissed here, I should point out that at the time their work was done, the difficulties of the second type of theory were not clearly understood.)

The Next Two Types

The theories we have been considering until now have all attempted to introduce U(6) as a symmetry in the usual sense — the same sense in which U(3) is an approximate symmetry of the strong interactions. The next two types of theories are subtler and deeper; they attempt to enlarge the idea of symmetry and to introduce groups of transformations that, although not directly connected with unitary transformations commuting with the S-matrix, nevertheless restrict scattering amplitudes.

Sixth Type: Subsidiary Conditions

Let us consider a theory (either a Lagrangian field theory or a purely phenomenological S-matrix theory) defined in a Hilbert space $\mathscr{H}$, which is not identified with the space of physical states. The space of physical states is a subspace, $\mathscr{H}_p$, of $\mathscr{H}$. The S-matrix, defined in $\mathscr{H}$, is symmetric under the action of a group G of the sort discussed in connection with the second type of theory. The physically observable S-matrix, however, is this operator evaluated between physical states. (We do something similar to this, though without the symmetry, when we construct theories of massive vector mesons in Gupta-Bleuler gauge. The physical Hilbert space is the space of all states with no longitudinally polarized mesons.) If $\mathscr{H}_p$ is not invariant under the action of G, the physical S-matrix is not invariant; however, it may still be severely restricted by the invariance of the original S-matrix. I will give two example.

1. (Beg and Pais; Sakita and Wali). The following free Lagrange density,

$$\mathscr{L} = \partial_\mu \overline{\psi} \partial^\mu \psi + m^2 \overline{\psi} \psi ,$$

where ψ is a quark field, is manifestly invariant under U(6, 6) ⊗ P', and it is trivial to construct, in the Hilbert space defined by $\mathscr{L}$, S-operators invariant under this group. Because the quadratic form $\overline{\psi}\psi$ is not positive definite, the creation operators associated with some of the modes of the quark field create states of negative norm; these cannot be physical. We may define the physical Hilbert space as the set of all states made by applying positive-norm quanta to the vacuum, and then use the general prescription stated earlier.

2. (Rühl). Here we use a group like the second one discussed in connection with theories of type two — a group with extra translations built from SL(6, C). The physical Hilbert space is defined as the set of states for which all but the first four momentum operators have value zero.

The trouble with these theories is that they restrict the physical S-matrix <u>too</u> severely; no S-matrix constructed according to these prescriptions is unitary, except for the trivial S-matrix. This result — no scattering — is similar to that which holds for theories of the fourth type, except there it is not necessary to impose the condition of unitarity.

At first glance, this loss of unitarity may seem obvious. If there is any scattering at all from physical states to unphysical states, application of the subsidiary condition would cause loss of probability. This argument, however, depends on the implicit assumption that the original S-matrix is unitary; in these two theories, the restricted S-matrix is nonunitary even if this assumption is not applied.

It should be remarked that in the Beg-Pais theory it is sufficient to consider quark-superscalar scattering to prove nonunitarity. (A superscalar is a particle with all quantum numbers zero.) For the Rühl theory it is necessary to go to the more complicated case of quark-quark scattering.

Again, it is not known if this difficulty occurs in all subsidiary-condition theories. Third unsolved problem for mathematicians: Prove that subsidiary conditions always lead to a breakdown of unitarity (if they restrict the S-matrix at all) or find a counter-example.

Seventh Type: Dashen-Gell-Mann Scheme

I will describe this last type in somewhat more detail than its predecessors, both because it is more complex and requires a fuller exposition, and because it contains many ingenious features that I suspect will survive into future theories.

Dashen and Gell-Mann begin with the familiar quark model and consider the set of all currents, that is to say, the set of all forms

$$j^{\alpha} = \psi^{+} M^{\alpha} \psi,$$

where M^{α} runs through the set of all 12×12 Hermitian matrices. These may be arranged in the usual way into the components of tensors, vectors, axial vectors, scalars, and pseudoscalars; but for our purposes it is more convenient to consider all 144 currents collectively. The equal-time space integrals of the currents,

$$G^{\alpha} = \int \partial^{3}\underset{\sim}{x}\, j^{\alpha}(\underset{\sim}{x}, 0),$$

form the generators of a Lie group, isomorphic to U(12). This group is called "the group of the currents" (more properly, "the group of integrated current components"). Note that the structure of the group is independent of the interaction Lagrangian, provided it contains no derivatives. Thus in order to obtain dynamical information from this group, we must make additional assumptions.

The first assumption is that the positive-parity subgroup of this group — a group isomorphic to $U(6) \otimes U(6)$, called "the static group" — turns one particle states at rest into one-particle states at rest. (We assume all resonances are stable.) Thus the one-particle states form representations of the static group. The octet and decuplet are put into a $(1,56)$, their antiparticles into a $(\overline{56},1)$, and the low-lying bosons into a $(6,\overline{6})$, which contains the nonrelativistic 35 plus an additional pseudoscalar singlet.

To go further, it is necessary to investigate the transformation properties of moving states. If we assume all the masses within a supermultiplet are degenerate, it is possible to gain partial information about this from the preceding assumption. The matrix element of the G's between stationary states may be written in terms of the invariant form factors for the j's, evaluated at zero momentum transfer. The matrix elements of the G's evaluated between moving states involve precisely the same form factors at the same point; thus they are essentially the same numbers, aside from kinematic factors depending on the Lorentz transformation properties of the j's and the momentum of the states. If one calculates these matrix elements, one finds that it is inconsistent to assume that the entire static group turns moving one-particle states into moving one-particle states; however, one can always find a subgroup, depending only on the direction of motion, for which the assumption is consistent. Dashen and Gell-Mann therefore make this assumption for this subgroup. The subgroup is always isomorphic to U(6), and is called "the collinear group." (Although I emphasize that it is a different subgroup of the static group for every direction of motion.) This group is formally the same as the $U(6)_W$ group found by Lipkin and Meshkov within the framework of the type six Beg-Pais theory.

This produces a very peculiar situation. If we have a process in which all momenta are aligned, such as a vertex function in the Breit frame or forward scattering in the center-of-mass frame, the maximum possible symmetry is the collinear group for that direction of motion. However, if we have a process in which there are two independent directions of motion, such as nonforward elastic scattering, the maximum possible symmetry group is the intersection of the two collinear groups for the two directions. This group depends only on the plane defined by the two directions; it is called "the coplanar group," and is isomorphic to $U(3) \otimes U(3)$. Finally, if we have a process with three independent directions, such as $\overline{N} + N \rightarrow 3\pi$, the maximum possible symmetry is the intersection of the three collinear groups, which is just ordinary U(3). (It is assumed in applications that all these maximum symmetries are attained.)

This is the characteristic feature of the seventh type: a diminishing hierarchy of symmetry groups, arranged in such a way that the more complicated the kinematics of a process, the less symmetry it has. The only group that is a symmetry of every process — a symmetry of the Lagrangian in the old sense — is U(3). Thus the difficulties of type two are completely avoided, while enough symmetry is retained to obtain all the attractive U(6) results for vertices and forward scattering.

(It has been pointed out that a diminishing hierarchy also occurs in theories of the sixth type. The projection operator on physical one-particle states can be written in the form

$$P = \int P(\underset{\sim}{k})d^3\underset{\sim}{k},$$

where $P(\underset{\sim}{k})$ is a projection operator acting only on states with momentum $\underset{\sim}{k}$. The projection operator for n-particle states is the tensor product of n one-particle projection operators. Thus, in a scattering process, those elements of the symmetry group that commute with the P(k)'s associated with all the momenta involved will be actual symmetries of the scattering amplitude. In this way we construct the diminishing hierarchy. However, in theories of the sixth type, there may be restrictions on the scattering amplitude beyond those given by the hierarchy. For example, in the Beg-Pais theory explained earlier, the hierarchy is the same as in the Dashen-Gell-Mann scheme. However, if, for example, we put the mesons in a 143-component field, the Beg-Pais theory allows only one quark-antiquark-meson coupling, while the collinear group allows two. Thus, even on the phenomenological level, the two theories are not equivalent.)

Unfortunately, it may be shown that the first two assumptions (invariance of the moving states under the collinear group), together with the usual axioms of local field theory, lead to the result that the generators of the collinear group commute with the full Hamiltonian. Thus the full symmetry of the world is not the intersection of the collinear groups but their union, and the scheme contains an internal contradiction.

The proof is somewhat involved, and I shall not even sketch it here; however, I should remark that although, like many arguments from the axioms, it involves analytic continuation, nevertheless the contradiction is insensitive, in the sense that it persists even if the Dashen-Gell-Mann assumptions are only approximately true.

Possible Eighth Types: The Spirit of U(6) Yet To Come

What is to be done? Can anything be salvaged from these ruins? One possible line of retreat is to accept the consequences of the Dashen-Gell-Mann scheme but not its foundations. We can retain the diminishing hierarchy of symmetry groups but abandon the identification of the group generators with the space integrals of local currents. In this way, we avoid the contradiction of the original theory, but the approach is in many ways unsatisfying. The descent from the static group, to the collinear group, to the coplanar group, which formerly followed from the transformation properties of the currents, must be made an independent postulate. Also the group of the currents is now isomorphic to the group of symmetries of the S-matrix, although completely unrelated to it dynamically — an extremely unsatisfactory state of affairs.

Another approach, and a more promising one, is based on the idea of saturation of commutators. Consider the commutator of two generators of the static group, evaluated between one-particle states at rest,

$$\langle\vec{0}|[G^{\alpha}, G^{\beta}]|\vec{0}\rangle .$$

We may write this in terms of a complete set of states,

$$\sum_{n} \langle\vec{0}|G^{\alpha}|n\rangle\langle n|G^{\beta}|\vec{0}\rangle - \langle\vec{0}|G^{\beta}|n\rangle\langle n|G^{\alpha}|\vec{0}\rangle .$$

Now, if this sum has significant contributions only from one-particle states, the generators of the static group, restricted to these states, obey the same algebra as the unrestricted generators. Therefore we may arrange the one-particle states into $U(6) \otimes U(6)$ multiplets.

The assumption that this in fact occurs — that the sum in the commutator is well approximated by the contribution from one-particle intermediate states — is called "commutator saturation." Note that this is a weaker assumption than that of Dashen and Gell-Mann. If the assumptions of Dashen and Gell-Mann were true, every term in the sum, beyond the one-particle terms, would vanish. Commutator saturation merely requires the total of all these terms to vanish.

In the case of the free quark field, the commutator is saturated, even though the Dashen-Gell-Mann assumptions do not apply. There are large matrix elements of the generators between one-quark states and states containing two quarks and an antiquark, but these cancel in the commutator sum.

The results of the collinear group for vertices may be obtained in a similar way, by saturating the commutator of a generator of the collinear group and the appropriate current, evaluated between moving states.

This approach has the additional advantage of being closer to our intuitions about dynamics than the preceding one. Commutators of currents are closely related to the absorbtive parts of scattering amplitudes; it is not at all unreasonable that such objects should be dominated by the nearest singularities, that is to say, that the commutators should be saturated by the lowest states.

It is somewhat more difficult to reproduce the results of Type Seven theories for scattering processes. These could be obtained by saturating the commutator of two elements of the collinear group, evaluated between two-particle states, with two-particle states with the same momenta. However, these are not "nearest singularities" but merely isolated points in a continuum; although the formal argument goes through, the assumptions are much less satisfying dynamically.

A way out of this particular difficulty has been suggested by Harari and Lipkin. These authors have shown, in the case of baryon-meson scattering, that if the amplitude is dominated by the exchange of one or two mesons, and if the relevant vertices possess collinear symmetry, then the principle results of collinear symmetry (the famous Johnson-Treiman relations) are valid for the forward scattering amplitude. It is not necessary to make any assumptions about saturation of commutators between two-particle states.

To summarize the picture that seems to be emerging: Saturation of appropriate commutators yields collinear symmetry for vertices. This, combined with dynamical assumptions of a more usual sort, gives many of the results of collinear symmetry for forward scattering.

Of course there remain many unresolved points. It is unpleasant to assume saturation for each commutator individually, with no dynamical justification. Perhaps such justification will be found when the relation between commutator saturation and more familiar dynamical approximations is better understood. In this connection, an especially sticky point has been raised by Mandelstam. If saturation of the appropriate commutators arises from general dynamical principles, one should expect it to be true whether the fundamental field theory involves quark fields or baryon and meson fields. However, the algebra of currents is quite different in these two cases. (In the baryon-and-meson case, the currents corresponding to the beta-decay currents do not even form an algebraically closed set.) Thus one could determine whether there are fundamental quark fields simply by examining form factors at low energies — a surprising result, to say the least!

As always, the situation is both confused and hopeful. Perhaps this time the confusion will be removed without the hope going with it.

Appendix: Some Related Topics

1. The approach of Schwinger is, as usual, unique. Schwinger considers two Lagrangians: a fundamental Lagrangian, involving quarklike triplets, which gives an exact description of reality, and a phenomenological Lagrangian, involving baryon and meson fields, which gives only an approximate description. Schwinger attempts to show that, if the phenomenological particles are tightly bound multiquark systems, the coupling constants in the phenomenological Lagrangian obey certain symmetries, closely related to those given by U(6, 6).

Of course, if the calculational rules for phenomenological fields are the same as those for fundamental fields, this leads to the well-known difficulties of theories of the fifth type. However, at the moment, it is not known whether this is the case.

2. McGlinn's theorem [Phys. Rev. Letters, 12, 467 (1964)] is often cited in discussions of relativistic U(6). In fact, it does

not apply. The theorem places restrictions on groups whose algebras are the sum of a purely internal set of generators and the generators of the Poincaré group. Even in the nonrelativistic limit, the algebra of U(6) is not of this form.

The most general form of McGlinn's theorem is due to L. Michel [Phys. Rev., 137, B405 (1965)].

3. Another theorem which is often erroneously cited is that of O'Raifertaigh [Phys. Rev. Letters, 14, 575 (1965)]. The theorem states that if G is a connected Lie group containing the Poincaré group, then, in every irreducible unitary representation of G, the spectrum of $P_\mu P^\mu$ is either a single point or a continuum. This answers (in the negative) the question of whether mass formulas, such as the Gell-Mann-Okubo formula, can arise as exact consequences of symmetry groups. However, the theorem has no direct application to the problem of constructing a relativistic U(6) theory; we would be perfectly happy if all the particles in a U(6) supermultiplet were degenerate in mass, as long as they were finite in number.

Bibliography

This bibliography is representative, not exhaustive; it would require the talent of a Dunbar to compile an exhaustive one. Before omitted authors become indignant, they are advised to examine the text and see how I have represented included ones.

"Trieste Proceedings" refers to High-Energy Physics and Elementary Particles; Lectures Presented at a Seminar at Trieste, May-June 1965, International Atomic Energy Agency, Vienna, 1966.

Type One

Sakita, B., Phys. Rev., 136, B1756 (1964).

Gürsey, F., and L. A. Radicati, Phys. Rev. Letters, 13, 299 (1964).

Beg, M. A., B. W. Lee, and A. Pais, Phys. Rev. Letters, 13, 514 (1964) (magnetic moment ratio).

Johnson, K., and S. Treiman, Phys. Rev. Letters, 14, 189 (1965) (forward scattering).

Type Two

A survey of the literature is contained in the counterpaper:
Coleman, S., Phys. Rev., 138, B1262 (1965).

A similar theorem is proved in
Weinberg, S., Phys. Rev., 139, B597 (1965).

Type Three

Zumino, B., Trieste Proceedings.

Budini, P., and C. Fronsdal, ibid.

Type Four

Mahanthappa, K. T., and E. C. G. Sudarshan, Phys. Rev. Letters, 14, 459 (1965).

Riazuddin, and L. K. Pandit, ibid., p. 462.

Gürsey, F., Phys. Letters (Amsterdam), 14, 330 (1965).

Epstein, H. (unpublished).

The counterpaper is:
Jordan, T. F., Phys. Rev., 140, B776 (1965).

Type Five

Bardacki, K., J. Cornwall, P. Freund, and B. W. Lee, Phys. Rev. Letters, 13, 678 (1964); 14, 48 (1965); 14, 264 (1965).

Okubo, S., and R. E. Marshak, Phys. Rev. Letters, 13, 818 (1964); 14, 156 (1965).

I list the papers of the Trieste group here, although they actually span both this type and Types Four and Six (in fact, they discuss both varieties of Type Six).

Salam, A., Phys. Letters (Amsterdam), 13, 349 (1965).

Salam, A., R. Delbourgo, and J. Strathdee, Proc. Roy. Soc. (London), A284, 146 (1965).

Salam, A., R. Delbourgo, M. A. Rashid, and J. Strathdee, Proc. Roy. Soc. (London), A285, 312 (1965).

Salam, A., R. Delbourgo, M. A. Rashid, and J. Strathdee, Trieste Proceedings.

Type Six

Beg, M. A., and A. Pais, Phys. Rev. Letters, 14, 267 (1965).

Sakita, B., and K. C. Wali, Phys. Rev. Letters, 14, 404 (1965).

Rühl, W., Nuovo Cimento (10), 37, 302, 319 (1965); Trieste Proceedings.

The counterpapers are:
Beg, M. A. B., and A. Pais, Phys. Rev. Letters, 14, 509 (1965).

Blancenbecler, R., M. L. Goldberger, K. Johnson, and S. B. Treiman, Phys. Rev. Letters, 14, 518 (1965).

Type Seven

Dashen, R. F., and M. Gell-Mann, Phys. Letters (Amsterdam 17, 142, 145 (1965).

Feynman, R. P., M. Gell-Mann, and G. Zweig, Phys. Rev. Letters, 13, 678 (1964).

The counterpaper is:

Coleman, S., Phys. Letters (Amsterdam), 19, 144 (1965).

$U(6)_W$ is discussed in:

Lipkin, H. J., and S. Meshkov, Phys. Rev. Letters, 14, 670 (1965).

Type Eight (?)

The saturation of current commutators between states at rest was first published by B. W. Lee, Phys. Rev. Letters, 14, 676 (1965). Similar ideas were being explored at the same time by R. Dashen and M. Gell-Mann (private communications).

None of the central ideas in this section of the text are my own. They have been gathered in conversations with M. A. Beg, J. Bell, R. Dashen, M. Gell-Mann, H. Harari, and S. Mandelstam.

The idea of collinear symmetry for vertices alone was proposed long before the connection with commutator saturation was known:

Barnes, K. J., P. Carruthers, and F. von Hippel, Phys. Rev. Letters, 14, 82 (1965).

Barnes, K. J., Phys. Rev. Letters, 14, 796 (1965).

Chapter 2

APPLICATIONS OF ALGEBRAIC TOPOLOGY TO PHYSICS

M. Froissart

1. Introduction

A problem very often encountered in physics these days in the study of integral formulas containing analytic functions with known singularities (Feynman integrals, unitarity relations, etc.). The basic problem is then to derive in turn the analytic properties of the integral, as functions of the parameters contained in the integrand. Several broad classes of questions may be asked, according to the more or less detailed information one wants. For example, one may wish to determine only possible places for singularities to occur, or the exact type of singularity occurring at a given place, or even the detailed structure of the Riemann surface of the integral. A more quantitative question is actually to find the increment of the function as one goes around the singularity in the space of parameters. Or it might be interesting to have only a broad knowledge of the geometry of such singularities "in the general case." All these problems are fairly easy to solve when the integration runs over one variable only and there is one parameter only; the problems do not require much geometrical insight. When the numbers of parameters and of variables of integration increase, however, it soon becomes difficult to "see" how one should distort the contours of integration as the parameters vary in order to prove or disprove analyticity.

2. Homology Theory: the Science of Integration Contours

To be specific, let the integral mentioned earlier read

$$I(t) = \int_C f(x, t)\, dx, \tag{1}$$

where

$x = (x_1, \cdots, x_n)$ denotes the n complex variables of integration: Space X
$dx = dx_1 \wedge dx_2 \wedge \cdots \wedge dx_n$
$t = (t_1, \cdots, t_p)$ denotes the p) complex parameters: Space T
f(x, t) is a function, analytic in x and t, except on a variety S of the (x, t) space Y where it is singular.
C is an oriented n-real-dimensional manifold of integration of Space X.

The main observation we can make about C in connection with the integral Equation 1 is that we expect to be able to distort C, by virtue of the analyticity of f(x, t) with respect to x. Indeed, this comes from Stokes's theorem. Let D be a manifold with n + 1 dimensions in X. Let ∂D be its boundary, suitably oriented; then

$$\int_{\partial D} f(x, t)\, dx = \int_D df \wedge dx = 0, \qquad (2)$$

if f is analytic everywhere on D. It is then intuitive, although by no means trivial, that one can define the "sum" of two contours by the formula

$$\int_{C_1} f\, dx + \int_{C_2} f\, dx = \int_{C_1+C_2} f\, dx.$$

It is understood, however, that parts of C_1 and C_2 which happen to overlap, but with the opposite orientation, "cancel" each other, as is familiar in the case of n = 1 (Figure 1). A precise definition is more involved than this crude sketch, which is, however, good enough for the purpose of introduction.

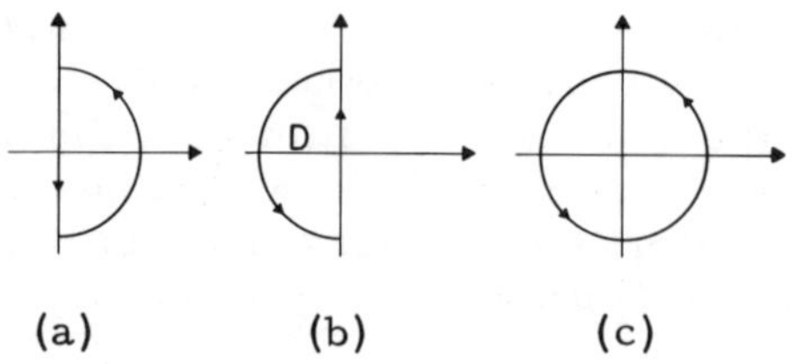

Figure 1. Addition of contours. (a) Contour C_1, (b) contour C_2, (c) contour $C = C_1 + C_2$.

We may thus consider any suitable[1] manifold of dimension 0 to 2n in X as being an element of an additive group K, a "chain."

[1]We consider here manifolds on which it makes sense to integrate, that is, for example, piecewise differentiable manifolds.

With this in mind, we see that the operation of "taking the oriented boundary" of a chain is a linear operation on the additive group K_p of chains of dimension p which gives a chain of dimension p - 1 (the boundary).

The operation of distortion of a contour may be written as

$$\int_{C+\partial D} f\,dx = \int_C f\,dx + \int_{\partial D} f\,dx = \int_C f\,dx \tag{3}$$

by virtue of Equation 2. See, for example, how the contour C_1 is distorted into $C = C_1 + C_2 = C_1 + \partial D$ on Figure 1. But this

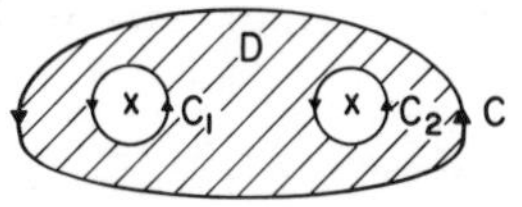

Figure 2. Decomposition of contour C by adding the boundary of D (shaded area).

operation may even go futher than distorting the contour, it may completely change its structure. In Figure 2, we have $C = C_1 + C_2 + \partial D$, and hence $\int_C = \int_{C_1} + \int_{C_2}$, if there is no singularity in D.

The aim of homology is to get rid of these rather trivial differences between contours. Homology classes are thus defined as classes of closed chains, two chains of any given class differing by a boundary.

In other words, among the many chains of dimension p, we select two families (subgroups of K_p): the family Z_p of closed chains (cycles) of dimension p: $\partial Z_p = 0$, and the family B_p of boundaries of (p + 1)-dimensional chains: $B_p = \partial K_{p+1}$. As $\partial^2 = 0$ (the boundary of a manifold does not have a boundary itself), B_p is indeed a subgroup of Z_p: We define the p-dimensional homology group as the quotient group $H_p = Z_p/B_p$.

In many practical cases H_p has only a finite number of generators, as opposed to K_p, Z_p, or B_p, which each have a nondenumerable set of generators. For example, if X is the two-dimensional plane of which a finite number of points have been taken out, a possible set of generators for H_1 is given by small oriented circles around each point. All other cycles may be decomposed into a sum of those with integer coefficients and the boundary of a two-dimensional chain D (Figure 2). This is the basis, for example, for the calculus of residues.

3. The Change of Contours as a Basis for Analytic Continuation

Let us come back to the integral I(t) in Equation 1. Assume, for simplicity, that the cycle of integration C is a closed, bounded chain: a compact cycle. It does not intersect the set of singularities S_{t_0} of f at the value t_0 from which we want to start the analytic continuation procedure. In general, if we move t in a sufficiently small neighborhood of t_0, the singular set S_t will not intersect C any more. We integrate on a compact cycle an analytic function of t; the integral is analytic. If we want to continue I(t) further, we may run into the difficulty that S_t and C meet. Then we choose another cycle C' of the homology class of C in the Space X - S_t. Any such cycle defines exactly the same integral, but we can prove analyticity in a different domain of T, for in general C' will not meet S_t for the same values of t as C. It is possible to go on with this procedure, alternating variation of t and variation of the cycle of integration. See, for example, Figure 3 for the analytic continuation of the integral

$$J(t) = \oint_C \frac{dx}{x^2 - t}$$

from $t_0 = 1$ to $t = 1$ after having completed a circle around the origin $t = 0$.

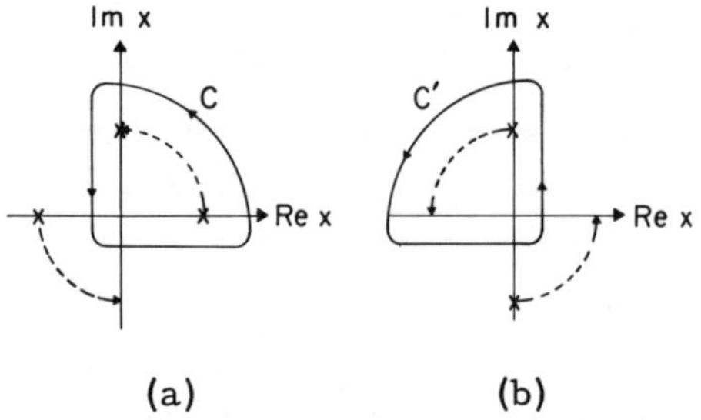

Figure 3. Analytic continuation of J(t) from t = 1 to t = 1 around t = 0.

This essentially amounts to following the class of homology of C by continuity as t varies. Thus the integral is analytic for all value of t for which this class continues to exist. In the opposite case, however, where this class disappears, we expect a singularity of I(t). This is the case, for example, for the integral J(t) at t = 0: all contours of the homology class of C are "pinche between both singularities as t goes to zero, and the class itself disappears at t = 0.

When does that occur? It is easier to answer first the question when does it <u>not</u> occur? For there is a fairly simple recipe, due to Thom, which gives a large set of points where no singularities occur. Let us outline it very sketchily, not going at all into details or strange situations.

Consider the whole set S of singularities of f(x, t) in the Space $Y = X \times T$. Decompose it into strata in essentially the following manner: Take all regular points of S. Each connected component of this set is a manifold of dimension n + p - 1. Call it a stratum of dimension n + p - 1. The remainder of S is the singular set of S. It is an analytic variety of dimension n + p - 2. Take all its regular points, they are divided into connected strata of dimension n + p - 2, and so on, taking each time the regular points of the preceding singular set.

For each stratum α, determine the critical set $C\alpha$, or set of points for which the projection of α in T is singular (the rank of the matrix of derivatives $\partial t_i/\partial Z_j$ is less than p, $\{Z_j\}$ being a set of coordinates on α). The projection of this critical set on T is called, according to usage in physics, the Landau set or "curve" $L\alpha$.

Thom's theorem now states that if X is bounded, the singularities may occur on Landau sets only. We may thus concentrate upon the study of I(t) near a Landau set. It is, however, impossible to discuss all possible cases. We shall limit ourselves to the "most likely" case, and give a more precise definition of what we understand by that.

4. Reflexions About the Phrase "In General"

Although there is no question here of defining "in general" by measure (or probability) theory, it is appropriate to recall the first difficulties encountered by students of probability theory when they have to pass from the discrete case to the continuous case. There is no invariant definition of uniform probability any more, and one has to consider how the random variable under consideration has been generated. The typical example of the distribution of length ℓ among the chords of a unit circle is well known: if the chord is generated by random uniform choice of the ends on the circle, the density function is $2/(\pi\sqrt{4 - \ell^2})$. If it is generated by random uniform choice of its middle inside the circle, the density function is $\ell/2$, and so on.

In a similar way, we shall define the generic features of a mathematical situation by a stability criterion with respect to some input data: the situation is generic if it still holds for any small modification of the input data.

For example, consider a plane curve. It may be defined by an equation

$$f(x, y) = 0. \tag{4}$$

The input data here is the function f. Such a curve does not have generic singular points, because the singular points, if they exist, do not go over to the curves $f(x, y) + \varepsilon = 0$.

Here we have modified a little the function f, by adding ε, and the singular point disappears. If we give the curve, however, by parametric equations

$$x = f(t) \qquad y = g(t), \tag{5}$$

it has self-crossing points as only generic singularities. The input data is the pair of functions f and g. If we modify them around a self-crossing point, the point may be displaced, but it does not disappear altogether as before. Of course, it is possible to eliminate t and get an equation of the form 4, but this is now a special subset of functions f(x, y) which corresponds to 5. The curve defined by Equation 5 does not have generic cusps, for if it has one at $t = t_0$, then $f'(t_0) = g'(t_0) = 0$. Change f(t) into $f(t) + \varepsilon(t - t_0)$, and the cusp disappears.

We can define a curve so that it has both generic self-crossing and cusps. This is the case for the envelope of the family of curves A_α

$$f(x, y, \alpha) = 0. \tag{6}$$

Our problem is to choose a way of defining the set S so that we may speak of generic properties. This choice has to be made according to the nature of the functions we encounter most frequently. In many problems, the function f(x, t) appearing in Equation 1 is a product of unrelated functions. So let us take as gener situation the case where S consists of a union of regular manifold $S^{(i)}$; each factor in f(x, t) may have singularities, but for each one the singular set will not in turn have singularities. This again, is arbitrary, but it occurs in many instances. Furthermore, we assume that the different factors are generically unrelated, that is, the different singular manifolds will not be, say, systematically tangent to each other.

With these assumptions, the different strata of S consist of the parts of the manifolds $S^{(i)}$ minus the intersections (dimension $n + p - 1$); then the intersections of two, $S^{(i)} \cap S^{(j)}$ minus the intersections with any other third (dimension $n + p - 2$), and so on.

To each of these strata will correspond a different Landau curve. Physicists are empirically very familiar with this kind of decomposition, which is the equivalent of what is known as "reduced graphs." The number of surfaces intersecting on the stratum of a given Landau "curve" is the number of internal lines left in the reduced graphs. The other ones are "contracted."

5. Generic Singularities Near a Landau "Curve"

Let us assume that the singularities of the integrand are poles only. Let (x_0, t_0) be a point of the critical set C^α of the stratum

$\alpha \subset S$. If dim $\alpha \leq$ dim (T) - 1, T being the space of parameters $t_1 \cdots t_p$, dim (T) = p, all points in α are critical, by the definition of critical. Hence dim (L_α) = dim (α). If this number is less than p by two or more units, L_α is an intersection of Landau curves of higher dimension. If dim α = p - 1, we have a situation known as the "linear pinch." One generator of the homology group disappears, but it is the same whichever way t goes around L_α. The integral is singular, but one-valued; hence its singularity is a pole. The Feynman graph of Figure 4 has a linear pinch as "leading singularity."

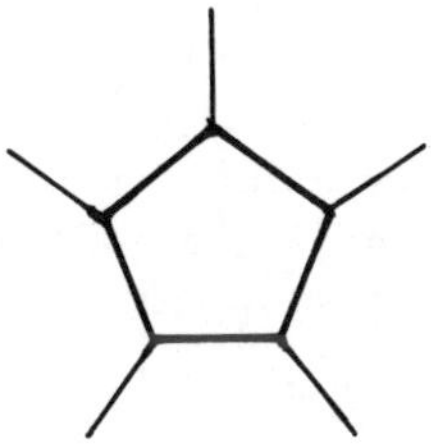

Figure 4. Simplest Feynman graph with a linear pinch.

In all other cases dim (α) > dim (C_α) = p - 1, we get the "quadratic pinch." This situation is more complicated than the former because the pinched generator of the homology group of X - S_t changes as t varies around L_α; if a pinched contour is followed by continuity as t makes a closed loop encircling L_α, it does not come back to its initial class of homology. This means that the integrals taken on it are not only singular but even several-valued. For example, see the integral J(t) and the related Figure 3. It is clear that, as Arg (t) goes from 0 to 2π, $|t| = 1$, the class of cycle C changes. An explicit evaluation of the integral gives indeed $J(t) = \pi i/\sqrt{t}$, which is clearly two-valued around t = 0.

A general study of the quadratic pinch gives the following results:

If dim (α) - dim (C_α) is odd, the singularity is quadratic: All elements of the homology group of X - S_t come back to their initial value when t completes two closed loops around L_α. This is the case for J(t): x is the manifold $x^2 - t = 0$

If dim (α) - dim (C_α) is even, the singularity is logarithmic: As t goes around L_α, each element of the homology group is increased by a certain amount.

In more quantitative terms, one would like to know what is the singularity of I(t) at t_0. Formulas have been evolved to answer this question in a systematic fashion. The first question is to know whether the particular cycle of integration is pinched, and how many times. This is done by computing the number N of points of intersection of the cycle of integration with a standard manifold, defined for each type of pinch. These points have to be added algebraically, the signs depending upon the orientations.

If this is done for all generators of the homology group and all Landau singularities, it is possible to determine how the integral on any contour will change as t varies. It defines in fact a Riemann surface on which all integrals are defined and one-valued.

Another interesting feature to investigate is the expression for the discontinuity of the integral as one goes around a Landau curve. A striking result is that the discontinuity around the Landau curve corresponding to the intersection $S^{(1)} \cap \cdots \cap S^{(m)}$ is given, up to a constant factor, by formally replacing the product of poles $[1/s_1(x,t)] \times \cdots \times [1/s_m(x,t)]$ by the expression $\delta[s_1(x,t)] \times \cdots \times \delta[s_m(x,t)]$ and integrating over $S^{(1)} \cap \cdots \cap S^{(m)}$ The constant factor contains, of course, the number N of times the contour is pinched. This is derived from a generalization to n variables of the calculus of residues, due to Leray. It corresponds to the prescription, well known to physicists, to calculate the same quantities by "putting on the mass-shell" all lines not contracted in the reduced diagram.

6. Geometrical Properties of the Landau "Curves"

The generic singularities of Landau curves are the generic singularities of envelopes in space T. In two dimensions, envelopes have generically self-crossing points and cusps. In three dimensions (p = 3), the Landau "surfaces" have self-crossing line and cusp ridges, which give back the singularities for p = 2 if on parameter is held fixed. Furthermore they have a new type of singularity, knotting these lines together (Figure 5). As the number of parameters increases, these singularities become more an

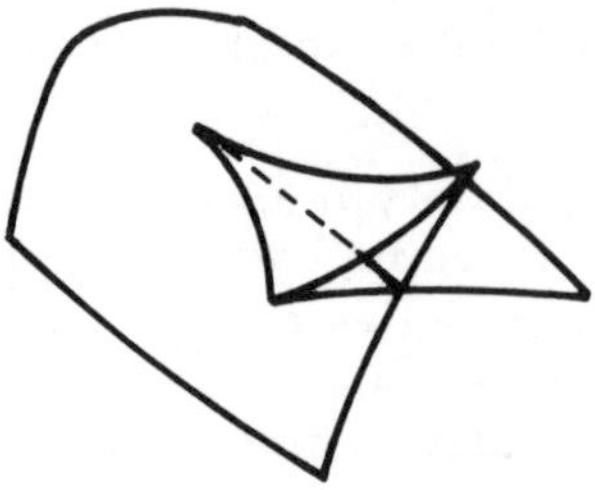

Figure 5. Singularity of a Landau "surface" in three dimensions.

more complex. These types of singularities have been encounter and were quite a surprise for the first investigators. We have no a more direct view of their very general character.

The relationship of Landau curves with one another is also explained by the very construction we outlined. Consider a stratum α contained in the closure $\overline{\beta}$ of another stratum β; for example,

α refers to the intersection of the same surfaces as β, with one more surface. ("α refers to a contraction of the reduced diagram of β.") In this case all points of α on $\overline{C\beta}$ are critical points of α: By continuity, the rank of the matrix of partial derivatives is still p - 1 there, and the tangent space to L_α is the limit of the tangent space to L_β. Therefore, L_α and L_β are tangent at each of their "effective" intersections, that is at points which are projections of one point of $\alpha \cap \overline{C\beta}$. It may be, of course, that L_α, L_β intersect at a point t_0 with C_α and C_β at different places in X-space. In this case they intersect at finite angle in general. This explains, however, the frequent occurrence of Landau curves tangent to each other.

7. Generalizations

All we have said refers to the simplest case. We have made a number of simplifying assumptions. These are met in a number of integrals, such as unitarity integrals. Let us see which of them have to be released and what to do in that case.

Closed Contours

In many cases the contour of integration is not closed. It is necessary then to redefine the homology in such a way as to include chains with the given boundary, up to the possibility of distorting the boundary along analytic surfaces.

Infinite X Space

If the Space X is infinite, it is not possible any more to use Thom's prescriptions. One way around this is to add "points at infinity" so that X is imbedded into a closed bounded analytic manifold, for example, a projective space. Care must be taken then to study the analyticity of the integrand at infinity. It may very well happen that it is not analytic at infinity. This new singularity has to be taken explicitly into account.

Correlation Between Singularities

In many cases, the assumption regarding the components of S, that they are not correlated, is not satisfied. A typical example is given by Feynman integrals, where several denominators may have the same "curve at infinity" if the compactification of X-space is carried out without sophistication into a projective space. This may be corrected by changing the space X into another space, such that this correlation is lost. This transformation may again introduce singular Jacobians.

Nonuniform Integrand

The case where the integrand is not uniform may also be treated. The residue calculation does not apply any more to the evaluation of the discontinuity, nor does the result on the type of singularity. However, it is possible to express the discontinuity around any Landau set in terms of the corresponding discontinuities of the factors in the integrand.

8. Conclusion

The mathematical tools presented in this paper are still only a basis for a systematic study of integrals. We may distinguish two aspects of the question: the mathematical side and the applied side. The former deals with the justification of the methods and the proof of very general theorems such as those of Picard, Lefshetz, Leray, or Thom. This has recently attracted the attention of leading mathematicians, from different points of view and it develops rapidly. The applied side of the question, however, deals with the practical methods of computation, or algorithms, best suited to special situations often encountered in actual problems. This is still in a very early stage of development. It is even fairly difficult to assess, for the moment, what the practicality of the scheme is, and how it compares with the more artisanal methods of old. The latter will obviously keep their value for simple cases.

I would like to end this by mentioning the names of D. Fotiadi and J. Lascoux, and especially F. Pham, who have gathered the difficult mathematical material and extracted from it something understandable for the physicist. A more detailed account on the present state of the question may be found in F. Pham's thesis at the University of Paris.

Chapter 3

PARAFIELD THEORY

O. W. Greenberg

1. Introduction

Among the outstanding differences between present-day quantum mechanics and classical mechanics is the symmetrization postulate that quantum mechanical states of more than one identical particle must be either symmetric (bosons) or antisymmetric (fermions) under permutations. Perhaps the earliest precursor of the symmetrization postulate was Gibbs's distinction between generic and specific phases, and his introduction of the factor $(N!)^{-1}$ in the partition function in order to resolve the paradox he pointed out concerning the possible entropy of diffusion of a gas of identical particles into itself [8]. Some of the first applications of the symmetrization postulate were to statistical problems, for example, the Bose-Einstein statistics for the photon gas in a blackbody cavity, and the Fermi-Dirac statistics for the electron gas in a metal. I suppose it is because of these early applications of the symmetrization postulate that one talks about the "statistics" of particles, rather than their "permutation symmetry," which I think would be more appropriate.

On first hearing about Bose and Fermi particles, any inquisitive student is likely to wonder whether there are any other types of permutation symmetry for particles, and, if so, if they occur in nature. This question can be explored theoretically in two different frameworks, quantum mechanics and quantum field theory. (Let me remark parenthetically that the equivalence of these two frameworks for Bose and Fermi particles is transparent, but for more general types of particles the relation between the two frameworks is not yet understood. I will say more about this later.)

In the quantum mechanical framework, the symmetrization postulate says that allowed states belong to one-dimensional representations of the permutation group. The obvious thing to do is to try to use the higher-dimensional (irreducible) representations of the permutation group to describe particles having general permutation symmetry. There seems to be no a priori objection to such a scheme provided certain changes, such as the replacement of a ray by a many-dimensional generalized ray as the description of a state, are made in the usual formalism of quantum mechanics. This scheme is described in Reference 16, which also contains a discussion of direct experimental tests of the symmetrization postulate.

The quantum field theory approach to particles not obeying the symmetrization postulate is called parafield theory or parastatistics.[1] This will be the subject of the rest of my talk. I will conclude these introductory observations with two remarks. The first is that the fields play two different roles in quantum field theory: (a) to construct states by acting polynomial-wise on the cyclic vacuum state, and (b) to allow the construction of local observables, that is, Hermitian operators, such as the current operator, which commute at spacelike separation. As I shall describe in what follows, parafields can play both of these roles, and, what is more, allow new possibilities in each role. A priori quantum theory requirements should be imposed only on the expectation values of observables in states. Except for fields which like the electromagnetic field, have a classical limit, fields are not observable. This is as true for charged fields or Fermi fields as for parafields. What is relevant is that all of these fields can be used to construct local observables. My second and concluding remark (which will be illustrated by the rest of this talk) is that parafield theories exist, and therefore no a priori argument against the existence of particles or fields other than bosons or fermions can be accepted until it has contended with the known example of parafield theory.

2. Green's Motivation for His Trilinear Commutation Relations

For free Bose or Fermi particles, the observables such as the Hamiltonian (energy) operator, momentum operator, and so on, can all be constructed in a simple way starting from the number operators

$$n_k = a_k^\dagger a_k, \qquad (1)$$

where a_k and $a_k^\dagger$ are the annihilation and creation operators for a particle in quantum state k. These operators obey the commutation relations

$$[a_k, a_\ell^\dagger]_\mp = \delta_{k\ell}, \qquad [a_k, a_\ell]_\mp = [a_k^\dagger, a_\ell^\dagger]_\mp = 0, \qquad (2)$$

[1] This theory was invented by H. S. Green [9].

where $[A, B]_{\mp} = AB \mp BA$, and the upper (lower) sign holds for Bose (Fermi) particles. The representation of these relations most commonly used in physics, the Fock representation, is characterized by

$$a_k \Phi_0 = 0, \tag{3}$$

where Φ_0 is the cyclic no-particle vector. From Equations 1 and 2 follow the commutation relations

$$[n_k, a_\ell]_- = -\delta_{k\ell} a_\ell, \qquad [n_k, a_\ell^\dagger]_- = \delta_{k\ell} a_\ell^\dagger \tag{4}$$

and

$$[n_k, n_\ell]_- = 0, \tag{5}$$

and from Equations 3, 4, and 2 it follows that the n_k have integer eigenvalues, 0, 1, 2, $\cdots$ for Bose particles, and 0, 1 for Fermi particles, which is the reason they are called "number" operators. It is interesting that the definition, Equation 1, and the commutation relations, Equations 4 and 5, of the number operators are the same for both the Bose and Fermi cases. It is well known that the Bose or Fermi commutation relations lead to many particle states which are symmetric or antisymmetric, respectively, under permutations.

Green found other methods of quantization which allow many particle states that do not obey the symmetrization postulate. He used the definition and commutation relations of the number operators as a clue and realized that the important properties of quantization follow from Equation 4, so that any change in the definition of the number operators which preserves Equation 4 will lead to an interesting quantization scheme. Green replaced the definition of the number operators, Equation 1, by

$$n_k = \frac{1}{2}[a_k^\dagger, a_k]_\pm + \text{const}, \tag{6}$$

where here, and from now on, the upper (lower) sign refers to the generalization of Bose (Fermi) quantization which we call para-Bose (para-Fermi.) With Equations 4 and 6 as a guide, Green wrote down a stronger set of trilinear commutation relations that are accepted as the basic parafield commutation relations:

$$[[a_k^\dagger, a_\ell]_\pm, a_m]_- = -2\delta_{km} a_\ell, \tag{7}$$

$$[[a_k, a_\ell]_\pm, a_m]_- = 0, \tag{8}$$

from which

$$[[a_k, a_\ell]_\pm, a_m^\dagger]_- = 2\delta_{\ell m} a_k \pm 2\delta_{km} a_\ell$$

follows by Jacobi's identity

$$[[A, B]_\pm, C]_- + [[B, C]_\pm, A]_- + [[C, A]_\pm, B]_- = 0,$$

and from which still other relations follow by taking the adjoint of both sides of the preceding equations. The commutative property of the number operators, Equation 5, follows from Equations 6, 7, and 8.

3. Classification of Fock Representations of Green's Trilinear Commutation Relations

For the Bose and Fermi commutation relations when there are an infinite number of degrees of freedom, that is, the index k that labels the creation and annihilation operators runs over an infinite set, an additional condition must be added to single out a unique unitary equivalence class of representations in a Hilbert space. The representation of most interest for quantum physics, the Fock representation, is characterized by the existence of a unique no-particle vector Φ_0 satisfying Equation 3 [7]. I want to study the Fock para-Bose and para-Fermi representations of Green's commutation rules, which are defined to be those which have such a unique no-particle vector Φ_0. Unlike the Bose and Fermi cases, the existence of a unique no-particle vector does not characterize a unique representation for the para-Bose and para-Fermi cases. Before giving the classification of the parafield representations, I shall restate the problem in more abstract language.

Consider the associative free *-algebras generated by polynomials in the elements a_k and $a_k^\dagger$. Consider the quotients of these algebras by the two-sided ideals generated by

$$[[a_k^\dagger, a_\ell]_\pm, a_m]_- + 2\delta_{km} a_\ell \tag{9}$$

and

$$[[a_k, a_\ell]_\pm, a_m]_-. \tag{10}$$

These quotient algebras are called the para-Bose and para-Fermi algebras. Look for all irreducible representations ρ of these algebras, in a Hilbert space, which have a left ideal generated by

$$\rho(a_k)\Phi_0 = 0,$$

with Φ_0 unique. These representations are classified (up to unitary equivalence) as follows: All such representations contain another left ideal generated by

$$[\rho_p(a_k)\rho_p(a_\ell^\dagger) - p\delta_{k\ell}]\Phi_0 = 0 \tag{11}$$

for some integer p, which characterizes the irreducible representation ρ_p of order p. I shall not reproduce the demonstration of this classification, which is contained in Reference 12. The number operator in ρ_p is

$$\rho_p(n_k) = \frac{1}{2}[\rho_p(a_k^\dagger), \rho_p(a_k)]_\pm \mp \frac{1}{2} p.$$

In addition, it follows from Green's ansatz (to be discussed later) that the representation of order p contains the two-sided ideal generated by

$$\sum \eta_Q \prod_{j=1}^{p+1} \rho_p(a_{\mu_j}^{(\dagger)}), \qquad \eta_Q = \begin{cases} \delta_Q, & \text{para-Bose,} \\ 1, & \text{para-Fermi,} \end{cases} \tag{12}$$

where Q is the permutation from (1, 2, $\cdots$, p + 1) to (μ_1, μ_2, $\cdots$, μ_{p+1}), δ_Q is the signature of Q, and the dagger in parentheses is meant to indicate that any combination of a's and $a^\dagger$'s can occur. It is tempting to conjecture that the maximal two-sided ideal contained in the representation ρ_p is generated by Equations 9, 10, and 12, and that this maximal ideal characterizes the representation. Finally, for p = 1, the para-Bose and para-Fermi Fock representations coincide with the Bose and Fermi Fock representations, so that parafields include ordinary fields as a special case.

The case where several different fields are present is important for physical applications but has no new mathematical features. To show the variety of possibilities that can occur, I shall state the possible relative commutation relations among different fields in physicists' language. Let me remind you that a pair of ordinary fields can either commute or anticommute (at spacelike separation — this will always be the case and will not be repeated). In the "normal" case for ordinary fields, a pair of fields commutes unless they are both Fermi fields, in which case they anticommute. The "anomalous" cases for ordinary fields differ from the normal case by the replacement of some commutators by anticommutators, and vice versa. The normal case is the general one; any anomalous case is equivalent to the normal case supplemented by some absolute conservation laws, modulo two.[2,3]

For parafields a pair of fields can have four kinds of relative commutation relations: they can commute (relative Bose) or anticommute (relative Fermi) or they can have relative (trilinear) para-Bose or para-Fermi commutation relations. The relative para relations are only allowed if both parafields have the same order, and are equivalent to ordinary relative commutation relations only for $p = 1$. No new possibility occurs for sets of three or more fields. The "normal" case is the one in which all fields of a given order have relative (trilinear) para commutation relations and the relative commutation relations are of Fermi type only when both fields are Fermi or para-Fermi. We call all other cases "anomalous"; in general they are restricted by some additional absolute conservation laws.

4. Relation Between Parafield Theory and Representations of the Permutation Group

For Bose and Fermi particles the relation between the quantum mechanical and quantum field theory descriptions is transparent. Let Ψ_N be a normalized N-particle state in the field theory Hilbert space $\mathscr{H}_{FT}$. Then

$$\Psi_N = (N!)^{-\frac{1}{2}} \int \prod_{i=1}^{N} d^3k_i\, f^{(N)}(\vec{k}_1, \vec{k}_2, \cdots, \vec{k}_N) \prod_{j=1}^{N} a^{\dagger}_{\vec{k}_j} \Phi_0,$$

where $\{\vec{k}_j\}$ are the momenta of the particles. The normalization $\|\Psi_N\| = 1$ implies the normalization

$$\|f^{(N)}\|^2 = \int \prod_{i=1}^{N} d^3k_i\, |f^{(N)}(\vec{k}_1, \vec{k}_2, \cdots, \vec{k}_N)|^2 = 1$$

for $f^{(N)}$. Define improper basis vectors

$$\Phi_N(\vec{k}_1, \vec{k}_2, \cdots, \vec{k}_N) = (N!)^{-\frac{1}{2}} \prod_{i=1}^{N} a^{\dagger}_{\vec{k}_j} \Phi_0$$

in $\mathscr{H}_{FT}$. Then the vector in the quantum mechanical Hilbert space $\mathscr{H}_{QM}$ corresponding to Ψ_N is

---

[2]The Klein transformations [15], cited in Reference 2, transform the anomalous cases into the normal case.

[3]The anomalous cases and their conservation laws for ordinary fields are discussed in general by H. Araki [2].

$$f^{(N)}(\vec{k}_1, \vec{k}_2, \cdots, \vec{k}_N) = (\Phi_N(\vec{k}_1, \vec{k}_2, \cdots, \vec{k}_N), \Psi_N),$$

with the norm just given.

For Bose (Fermi) particles $f^{(N)}$ belongs to the identity (antisymmetric) representation of the permutation group on the N $\vec{k}_i$. The same permutation properties also hold in $\mathscr{H}_{FT}$; Ψ_N belongs to the same representations of the permutation group on the N $a^\dagger_{k_i}$ as $f^{(N)}$ does for the N $\vec{k}_i$.

For para-Bose and para-Fermi particles of order greater than one, we find a surprise: permutations of the creation operators that, acting on the vacuum, make the state no longer correspond to permutations of the particles in the quantum mechanical Hilbert space $\mathscr{H}_{QM}$. What is more, permutations of the particles are not represented at all in $\mathscr{H}_{FT}$! Galindo and Yndurain gave a simple example [6] which shows that permutations can not be represented on $\mathscr{H}_{FT}$. Let $a^\dagger_i$ be free para-Fermi creation operators of order 2. For this special case, the $a^\dagger_i$ satisfy the commutation relation

$$a^\dagger_i a^\dagger_j a^\dagger_k + a^\dagger_k a^\dagger_j a^\dagger_i = 0.$$

The state $\Psi = a^\dagger_j a^\dagger_j a^\dagger_k \Phi_0$ has positive norm; however $P_{(23)}\Psi = a^\dagger_j a^\dagger_k a^\dagger_j \Phi_0$ vanishes because of the above commutation relation. Thus permutations cannot be represented on $\mathscr{H}_{FT}$. As Galindo and Yndurain point out, this incompatibility of permutations with $\mathscr{H}_{FT}$ comes about because, in contrast to the situation for Bose and Fermi quantization, the two-sided ideals generated by the para-Bose and para-Fermi commutation relations, Equation 8 or 10, in the free algebra of the annihilation (or creation) operators, are not invariant under permutations of the annihilation (or creation) operators, so that permutations can neither be defined acting on the elements of the quotient algebras, which are the usual para annihilation (creation) operators, nor acting on $\mathscr{H}_{FT}$.

What then is the relation between $\mathscr{H}_{FT}$ and some $\mathscr{H}_{QM}$ on which permutations do act? I would like to put forward a conjecture about this: For para-Bose (para-Fermi) operators of order p, $\mathscr{H}_{FT}$ contains vectors that can be associated with every Young tableau with at most p rows (columns). The number of linearly independent vectors in $\mathscr{H}_{FT}$ associated with a given tableau equals the dimension of the irreducible representation of the permutation group associated with that tableau. However each vector in $\mathscr{H}_{FT}$ corresponds to an <u>entire</u> irreducible representation, belonging to the same Young tableau, in $\mathscr{H}_{QM}$. Thus, according to this conjecture, the redundancy associated with the generalized rays that represent states of particles which are not Bose or Fermi in

$\mathscr{H}_{QM}$ is removed in $\mathscr{H}_{FT}$ and at the same time the unobservable permutation operators are eliminated.

5. Green's Ansatz

Up to now I have discussed the parafields directly, without introducing any auxiliary mathematical objects. I did this to emphasize that no such auxiliary objects are necessary for parafield theory. Now I would like to tell you about a trick, due to Green [9], which introduces auxiliary objects, and which although not essential, is useful. Green noticed that he could construct operators satisfying his trilinear commutations relations, Equations 7 and 8, from the ordinary Bose and Fermi operators. His ansatz gives a para-Bose operator of order p as

$$a_k = \sum_{\alpha=1}^{p} b_k^{(\alpha)},$$

where for a given value of α the $b_k^{(\alpha)}$ and $b_k^{(\alpha)\dagger}$ are Bose operators,

$$[b_k^{(\alpha)}, b_\ell^{(\alpha)\dagger}]_- = \delta_{k\ell}, \qquad [b_k^{(\alpha)}, b_\ell^{(\alpha)}]_- = 0,$$

and for $\alpha \neq \beta$ all the operators anticommute,

$$[b_k^{(\alpha)}, b_\ell^{(\beta)\dagger}]_+ = [b_k^{(\alpha)}, b_\ell^{(\beta)}]_+ = 0, \qquad \alpha \neq \beta.$$

Para-Fermi operators of order p are constructed similarly, but with the roles of commutators and anticommutators interchanged. The Fock representation of the $b_k^{(\alpha)}$ and $b_k^{(\alpha)\dagger}$, for which

$$b_k^{(\alpha)} \Phi_0 = 0,$$

contains a reducible representation of the a_k and $a_k^\dagger$, one irreducible component of which is the Fock representation ρ_p that we discussed earlier. Using Green's ansatz, all calculations with free parafields can be reduced to calculations with free Bose and Fermi fields.

This approach is a simple way to see the physical interpretation of the order of a parafield. Consider the "symmetric" and "antisymmetric" states

$$\Psi_N^{(s)} = \sum_Q \prod_I^N a_{\mu_j}^\dagger \Phi_0$$

$$\Psi_N^{(a)} = \sum_Q \delta_Q \prod_1^N a_{\mu_j}^\dagger \, \Phi_0.$$

Using Green's ansatz it is easy to see that for order p parafermions $\Psi_N^{(s)} = 0$, if $N > p$, and for order p parabosons $\Psi_N^{(a)} = 0$, if $N > p$. Thus p is the maximum number of parafermions (parabosons) of order p which can occur in a "symmetric" ("antisymmetric") state. As a special case of this, any number of parabosons, but at most p parafermions of order p, can occupy the same quantum state.

It is straightforward to extend Green's ansatz to deal with several different parafields with some set of relative commutation relations between them.

6. High-Order Limit of Para-Bose and Para-Fermi Fields

I mentioned before that for $p = 1$ the parafields reduce to ordinary fields. It is amusing to ask what happens for $p \to \infty$. For each p, the representation is defined in a different Hilbert space, so some care should be taken in comparing fields of different order. One way to handle the problem is to use the positive linear functional on the representation given by the expectation value in the no-particle state; this approach was used in Reference 11. Here I want to describe the situation heuristically in physicists' language. First, Equation 11 implies that $\|\rho_p(a_k^\dagger)\,\Phi_0\|^2 = p$, so $\rho_p(a_k^\dagger)$ will not approach a limit for $p \to \infty$. However $c_k(p) \equiv p^{-\frac{1}{2}}\rho_p(a_k)$, and $c_k(p)^\dagger \equiv p^{-\frac{1}{2}}\rho_p(a_k^\dagger)$, whose commutation relations and no-particle conditions are

$$[[c_k(p)^\dagger, c_\ell(p)]_\pm, c_m(p)]_- = 2p^{-1}\delta_{km}c_\ell(p), \tag{13}$$

$$[[c_k(p), c_\ell(p)]_\pm, c_m(p)]_- = 0, \tag{14}$$

$$c_k(p)\,\Phi_0 = 0, \tag{15}$$

$$c_k(p)c_\ell(p)^\dagger\,\Phi_0 = \delta_{k\ell}\,\Phi_0, \tag{16}$$

do approach limits for $p \to \infty$. Heuristically, the right-hand side of Equation 13 vanishes for $p \to \infty$, so that $[c_k(p)^\dagger, c_\ell(p)]_\pm$ and $[c_k(p), c_\ell(p)]_\pm$ commute with all $c_m(p)$ and $c_m(p)^\dagger$ in the limit and thus are multiples of the identity. From Equation 16, this multiple can be evaluated; the result is

$$[c_k(p), c_\ell(p)^\dagger]_\pm = \delta_{k\ell}, \qquad [c_k(p), c_\ell(p)]_\pm = 0.$$

Thus the high-order limit of para-Bose fields satisfies Fermi commutation relations and the high-order limit of para-Fermi fields satisfies Bose commutation relations. At first sight this result raises a paradox concerning the spin-statistics theorem since the spin of the field does not change in the high-p limit; however no inconsistency occurs. This apparent paradox is discussed in detail in Reference 11, to which those whose curiosity is aroused sufficiently are referred.

7. General Parafield Theory

The TCP theorem and the connection of spin and type of commutation relations (para-Bose or para-Fermi) have been derived for parafields starting from the assumption that a general parafield can be represented by a Green ansatz in terms of general Bose or Fermi fields [5]. However, in contrast to free parafield theory in which Green's ansatz has been shown to hold without loss of generality [12], the status of Green's ansatz for general parafield theory is unclear, and the assumption of paralocality used in Reference 5 is too restrictive, so that this work can be regarded as only provisional.

8. Analysis of Local Observables Constructed from Parafields

Polynomials in ordinary free fields all taken at the same point will be local, that is, commute at spacelike separation, provided that an even number of Fermi fields occurs in each term. There is a greater variety of ways in which local operators can be constructed from such polynomials in free parafields. The derivation of general rules for such local operators starts from the demonstration [3] that an operator local in the Hilbert space generated by the parafields acting on the vacuum is also paralocal, that is, is local acting on the larger Hilbert space generated by the individual Green components acting on the vacuum. The analysis then makes systematic use of the expansion of the local operator in monomials in Green components. To handle the most general possibilities posed by many fields having some assortment of the four types of commutation rules for a field with itself as well as of the four types of relative commutation relations amo pairs of fields requires a detailed notation and a good deal of mod two arithmetic, both of which I shall spare you, since it is all written down in Reference 12. The result for the least restrictive case, the normal case, is that local polynomials in free parafields all taken at the same point can be formed in two different ways. The more obvious way is to copy the kind of local operators which occur in ordinary field theory. For example, for a charged para-Bose field $\phi(x)$ of any order

$$j^{\mu}(x) = \frac{i}{2}\left[\phi^*(x), \frac{\overleftrightarrow{\partial}}{\partial x_\mu}\phi(x)\right]_+ = i\sum_{\alpha=1}^{p} :\phi^{(\alpha)*}(x)\frac{\overleftrightarrow{\partial}}{\partial x_\mu}\phi^{(\alpha)}(x):,$$

where $A\overleftrightarrow{\partial}B = A\partial B - (\partial A)B$ and double dots indicate Wick ordering, is local, and for a charged para-Fermi field $\psi(x)$ of any order so is

$$j^{\mu}(x) = \frac{1}{2}[\overline{\psi}(x), \gamma^{\mu}\psi(x)]_- = \sum_{\alpha=1}^{p} :\overline{\psi}^{(\alpha)}(x)\gamma^{\mu}\psi^{(\alpha)}(x):.$$

Note that both of these are "diagonal" in the Green index α. The less obvious way to make local operators is to arrange to "saturate" the Green indices, that, is to form a polynomial of degree p in parafields of order p, which have relative para commutation relations, in such a way that each term in the expansion in Green component fields contains fields with each of the p possible values of the Green index. One example should make this clear. For order $p = 3$, let $\psi(x)$ be para-Fermi, $\phi(x)$ be para-Bose, and let ψ and ϕ have relative para-Bose commutation rules. Then

$$H_I(x) = \frac{1}{4}g[[\overline{\psi}(x), \psi(x)]_+ - \langle[\overline{\psi}(x), \psi(x)]_+\rangle_0, \phi(x)]_+$$

$$= g\sum_{\substack{\alpha_1,\alpha_2,\alpha_3\\ \text{all different}}} :\overline{\psi}^{(\alpha_1)}(x)\psi^{(\alpha_2)}(x)\phi^{(\alpha_3)}(x):,$$

where $\langle\ \ \rangle_0$ denotes vacuum expectation value, is local. The most general local operator can be formed from local operators of the two kinds just described.

The single most important consequence of the foregoing analysis is that the total degree of parafields of each order $p > 1$ in a local observable must be greater than one.

9. Selection Rules for the S Matrix

Starting from the assumption that the interaction Hamiltonian density is a local operator with all fields at the same point, and using the classification of such operators given above, selection rules for the S matrix can be derived. One way to do this is to look for selection rules that hold for all Feynman diagrams involving para particles. Standard perturbation theory holds when the parafields are expressed in terms of Green component fields. Each Feynman diagram with para particles then is replaced by a linear combination of diagrams having the same topology, but with lines associated with the Green component fields. I will again spare you the modulo two arithmetic, and just state the selection rules [12], valid to all orders of perturbation theory, which hold for reactions involving para particles:

1. The total number of Fermi-like particles, that is, fermions and parafermions, is absolutely conserved modulo 2. This rule is analogous to the usual selection rule for Bose and Fermi particles.

2a. For each even p, the total number of para particles of order p on both sides of a reaction must be even.

2b. For each odd p, the total number of para particles of order p on both sides of a reaction can take any value except for odd numbers smaller than p.

These rules give the possibilities which can occur for para particles. Note that 2b allows reactions in which the number of para particles of order p (for p odd) is not conserved modulo 2. There are examples in which each reaction allowed by these rules occurs

The single most important consequence of these selection rules is that reactions with any number of ordinary particles and only one para particle are absolutely forbidden.

10. Application to the Known Particles

The selection rule that prohibits reactions with only one para particle prohibits, in particular, the decay of a para particle into ordinary ones and the production of a single para particle by ordinary particles. This rule, together with some experimental information, shows that no particle known at present can be para [12, 14]. There is good experimental evidence that the nucleon and electron are Fermi and the photon is Bose. Pions are produced singly, for example, $N + N \to N + N + \pi$, so pions are ordinary. Hyperons and other mesons are ordinary because they decay into pions and nucleons; for example, $\Xi \to \Lambda + \pi \to N + 2\pi$, and $K^* \to K + \pi \to 3\pi, 4\pi$. Neutron decay, $n \to p + e + \nu_e$, shows that ν_e is ordinary. For the muon a more detailed argument is necessary to demonstrate that it is ordinary. Under the assumption that the electrodynamics of the muon is the same, except for mass, as that of the electron, the lowest order (in $\alpha = e^2/hc$), cross section for pair production of para muons of order p by photons in the external field of a nucleus is p times the corresponding cross section for Fermi muons. The $\mu\,\bar{\mu}$ photoproduction cross section has been measured to be 1.00 ± 0.05 times the cross section for Fermi muons [1], thus excluding the para cases $p \geq 2$. Given that μ is Fermi, pion decay shows that ν_μ is also Fermi. (If the two neutrinos in μ decay are both different from the ν_μ in π decay and the ν_e in β decay, then these μ-decay neutrinos might both be para. This possibility seems unlikely. Why should the only known para particles hide in such an obscure place as μ decay? A further objection to this possibility is that if, as is suggested by experimental evidence, the lepton fields enter the weak interaction Hamiltonian H_W via local currents, then the μ-decay neutrino fields ν_1 and ν_2 would have to enter H_W in a neutral current, and one would expect the unobserved decay $K^+ \rightarrow \pi^+ + \nu_1 + \nu_2$.[4])

11. Application to a Paraquark Model of Baryons and Mesons

A simple concrete basis for the regularities that appear when the observed particles are classified according to irreducible representations of SU(6) is the assumption that baryons and mesons are bound states of quarks, that the quarks transform as the fundamental representation of SU(6), and that the forces between quarks (and also antiquarks) are, at least in low-lying bound states, approximately independent of spin and unitary spin. Since in this model mesonic states are made from a quark and an antiquark, which are distinguishable, ordinary and parafield theory will lead to similar conclusions about mesonic states. This is not the case for baryonic states, which are made of three identical quarks. Analogy with the shell structure of atomic and nuclear physics suggests taking the three quarks in the lowest S-state for the ground state of the baryons.[5] Then the symmetry of these baryons under permutations of the quarks is given by the symmetry of the SU(6) three-quark wave function. If quarks are fermions, the antisymmetric 20-dimensional representation must be used [19]. However, this representation does not fit the known particles, and gives a wrong prediction for the proton-neutron magnetic moment ratio, so it must be rejected on experimental grounds. The representation which fits the observed spin $\frac{1}{2}$ octet and spin $\frac{3}{2}$ decuplet [13], for which accurate mass formulas can be found [13, 17],[6] and which predicts the proton-neutron magnetic moment ratio to be $-\frac{3}{2}$ (within three per cent of the experimental value) [4, 18], is the symmetric 56-dimensional representation. It is striking that this representation is symmetric, rather than antisymmetric, in violation of the Pauli exclusion principle. Parafield theory offers an explanation of this surprise. If quarks are para-Fermi particles of order three, then a symmetric state of three of them can be constructed, and this composite object is an effective Fermi particle [10]. Furthermore, this particle is

[4]I want to thank Professor A. Pais for a discussion of this point.

[5]"Nodeless" theorems do not hold when there are exchange forces.

[6]Many articles by many authors in Phys. Rev. Letters, Phys. Letters, and other journals give further SU(6) results.

the only ordinary particle that can be made from three paraquarks of order three; all other such three-body states are para particles. The effective Fermi operator, $f^{\dagger}_{\lambda\mu\nu}$, for Fermi baryons is

$$f^{\dagger}_{\lambda\mu\nu} = [[a^{\dagger}_{\lambda}, a^{\dagger}_{\mu}] \, , a^{\dagger}_{\nu}]_{+}$$

$$= 4 \sum_{\substack{\alpha,\beta,\gamma \\ \text{all different}}}^{3} a^{(\alpha)\dagger}_{\lambda} a^{(\beta)\dagger}_{\mu} a^{(\gamma)\dagger}_{\nu},$$

where a is a para-Fermi operator of order three, and λ, μ, ν are SU(6) indices. The state $f^{\dagger}_{\lambda\mu\nu} \Phi_0$ is symmetric under permutations, and is an effective Fermi state, since $[f^{\dagger}_{\lambda\mu\nu}, a^{\dagger}_{\sigma}]_{+} = 0$, which implies $[f^{\dagger}_{\lambda\mu\nu}, f^{\dagger}_{\sigma\tau\eta}]_{+} = 0$. I refer you to Reference 10 for further development of the paraquark model.

Acknowledgments

My understanding of parafield theory and related subjects has benefited greatly from joint work with Professor A. M. L. Messiah of Centre d'Etudes Nucléaires de Saclay. I am happy to thank Professor A. Pais for his warm hospitality at the Rockefeller University, and to thank the Alfred P. Sloan Foundation for its generous support. This research was also supported in part by National Science Foundation Grant GP 3221.

References

1. Alberigi-Quaranta, A., M. De Pretis, G. Marini, et al., "Photoproduction of Muon Pairs in Carbon," in Proceedings 1962 International Conference on High-Energy Physics at CERN, ed. J. Prentki, CERN, Geneva, 1962, pp. 469-473.

2. Araki, H., "On the Connection of Spin and Commutation Relations between Different Fields," J. Math. Phys., 2, 267-270 (1961).

3. Araki, H., O. W. Greenberg, and J. S. Toll, "Equivalence of Locality and Paralocality in Free Parafield Theory," Phys. Rev., 142, 1017-1018 (1966).

4. Bég, M. A. B., B. W. Lee, and A. Pais, "SU(6) and Electromagnetic Interactions," Phys. Rev. Letters, 13, 514-517 (1964).

5. Dell Antonio, G. F., O. W. Greenberg, and E. C. G. Sudarshan, "Parastatistics: Axiomatic Formulation, Connection of Spin and Statistics and TCP Theorem for a General Field Theory," in Group Theoretical Concepts and Methods in Elementary Particle Physics, ed. F. Gürsey, Gordon & Breach Publishers, Inc., New York, 1964, pp. 403-408.

6. Galindo, A., and F. J. Yndurain, "On Parastatistics," Nuovo Cimento, 30, 1040-1047 (1963), especially Footnote 4, p. 1041.

7. Gårding, L., and A. S. Wightman, "Representations of the Anticommutation Relations," and "Representations of the Commutation Relations," Proc. Nat. Acad. Sci., U.S., 40, 617-621, and 622-626 (1954).

8. Gibbs, J. W., Elementary Principles in Statistical Mechanics, in The Collected Works of J. Willard Gibbs, Yale University Press, New Haven, 1948, reprint, Chapter XV, especially pp. 206-207.

9. Green, H. S., "A Generalized Method of Field Quantization," Phys. Rev., 90, 270-273 (1953).

10. Greenberg, O. W., "Spin and Unitary-Spin Independence in a Paraquark Model of Baryons and Mesons," Phys. Rev. Letters, 13, 598-602 (1964).

11. Greenberg, O. W., and A. M. L. Messiah, "High-Order Limit of Para-Bose and Para-Fermi Fields," J. Math. Phys., 6, 500-504 (1965).

12. Greenberg, O. W., and A. M. L. Messiah, "Selection Rules for Parafields and the Absence of Para Particles in Nature," Phys. Rev., 138, B 1155-B 1167 (1965). Earlier work on parafield theory can be traced from references in this article.

13. Gürsey, F., and L. A. Radicatti, "Spin and Unitary Spin Independence of Strong Interactions," Phys. Rev. Letters, 13, 173-175 (1964).

14. Kamefuchi, S., and J. Strathdee, "A Generalization of Field Quantization and Statistics, (II) Interacting Fields," Nucl. Phys., 42, 166-176 (1963).

15. Klein, O., J. Phys. U.S.S.R., 9, 1 (1938).

16. Messiah, A. M. L., and O. W. Greenberg, "Symmetrization Postulate and Its Experimental Foundation," Phys. Rev., 136, B 248-B 267 (1964).

17. Pais, A., "Implications of Spin-Unitary Spin Independence," Phys. Rev. Letters, 13, 175-177 (1964).

18. Sakita, B., "Electromagnetic Properties of Baryons in the Supermultiplet Scheme of Elementary Particles," Phys. Rev. Letters, 13, 643-646 (1964).

19. Sakita, B., "Supermultiplets of Elementary Particles," Phys. Rev., 136, B 1756-B 1760 (1964).

Chapter 4

EXISTENCE THEOREMS FOR A CUT-OFF $\lambda\phi^4$ FIELD THEORY

Arthur Jaffe

We study a model for a quantum field, self-coupled with a nonlinear current. In particular, we investigate a massive, spin-zero field with a $\lambda\phi^4$ self-interaction, so that the total energy is formally positive. Hence, we wish to deal with the equation of motion

$$(\Box + \mu^2)\phi(\vec{x}, t) = -4\lambda\phi^3(x, t) + \delta m^2\phi(\vec{x}, t), \tag{1}$$

where $\phi(\vec{x}, t)$ is an operator-valued distribution. The plan is to use Hamiltonian methods to solve the initial value problem, and to require that the field satisfy the canonical, equal-time commutation relations. But then we know from Haag's theorem [3] that in order to write down a relativistic $\lambda\phi^4$ Hamiltonian as a bona fide operator, we must use a strange representation of the canonical commutation relations [1, 11, 13]. Since little is known about the structure of these representations, we shall study the theory in Fock space. Thus, in order to make sense of the Hamiltonian as an operator and to give a meaning to the nonlinear current that appears in Equation 1, we shall cut off the interaction Hamiltonian. It will then be shown that the cut-off total Hamiltonian H_K exists as an unbounded operator in Fock space, and is essentially self-adjoint on a natural domain D_0. Define an interacting field operator at time t by

$$\phi(f, t) = \exp(iH_K t)\phi(f)\exp(-iH_K t),$$

and (2)

$$\pi(f, t) = \exp(iH_K t)\pi(f)\exp(-iH_K t).$$

The operator $\phi(f)$ is a free field of mass μ restricted to the time $t = 0$, and $\pi(f)$ is the canonically conjugate free-field momentum. Let the domain of $\phi(f)$ be $D(\phi(f))$, then the initial domain of $\phi(f, t)$ will be

$$\exp(iH_K t)\, D(\phi(f)),$$

and similarly for $\pi(f, t)$. We study the closures of $\phi(f, t)$ and $\pi(f, t)$.

The Hamiltonian H_K has a unique ground state, or "physical vacuum," which we denote ψ_0. It is possible to apply Hilbert space methods in order to prove the existence of the vacuum expectation values of products of interacting fields, as well as the existence of the Green's functions (time-ordered vacuum expectation values). The vacuum expectation values and the Green's functions will each satisfy an infinite set of coupled partial differential equations, which can be interpreted in the sense of distributions. These equations are exactly the equations which formally follow from varying our cut-off Lagrangian in the old-fashioned manner.

We investigate several properties of the solutions. The vacuum expectation values are not analytic in the coupling constant λ at $\lambda = 0$. [5] However, there is analyticity in this theory in a neighborhood of every point on the real positive λ axis.

The techniques used here can also be adapted to study self-interactions among several coupled fields, or to study interactions that involve fields with spin, so long as the interaction Hamiltonian is suitably bounded below. We shall see that similar results do not follow for a $\lambda\phi^3$ interaction in which the energy spectrum formally extends down to minus infinity, and in this theory a corresponding set of expectation values does not exist.

Our ultimate goal is to remove the cut-off from the vacuum expectation values and to recover a relativistic field theory in the limit. Little will be said here about this next step, but in a final section we indicate how the complete program has been carried out in the case of a quadratic interaction Lagrangian.

1. The Basic Setup

The interaction picture field will be quantized in a box of volume V with periodic boundary conditions:

$$\phi(f) = \left(\frac{1}{2V}\right)^{\frac{1}{2}} \sum_{\vec{k}} [a(\vec{k})\hat{f}(\vec{k}) + a^*(\vec{k})\hat{f}(-\vec{k})]\, \omega(\vec{k})^{-\frac{1}{2}},$$

and

$$\pi(f) = -i\left(\frac{1}{2V}\right)^{\frac{1}{2}} \sum_{\vec{k}} [a(\vec{k})\hat{f}(\vec{k}) - a^*(\vec{k})\hat{f}(-\vec{k})]\, \omega(\vec{k})^{\frac{1}{2}}.$$

Here

$$\hat{f}(\vec{k}) = -\frac{1}{V^{\frac{1}{2}}} \int_V f(\vec{x})\, e^{i\vec{k}\vec{x}}\, d\vec{x},$$

$$\omega(\vec{k}) = (\vec{k}^2 + \mu^2)^{\frac{1}{2}},$$

$$[a(\vec{k}), a^*(\vec{k}')] = \delta_{\vec{k},\vec{k}'},$$

$$[a(\vec{k}), a(\vec{k}')] = 0,$$

and

$$\vec{k} = \frac{2\pi}{V^{\frac{1}{3}}}(\nu_1, \nu_2, \nu_3),$$

where ν_j are integers between $-\infty$ and ∞. The free-field Hamiltonian for mass μ is given by

$$H_0 = \frac{1}{2}\int_V : \{\pi^2(\vec{x}) + (\nabla\phi)^2(\vec{x}) + \mu^2\phi^2(\vec{x})\} : dx.$$

We define the total Hamiltonian to be

$$H_K = H_0 + H_I, \tag{3}$$

where the cut-off interaction Hamiltonian H_I can be expressed in terms of an energy density as

$$H_I = \lambda \int_{\substack{V \\ t=0}} : \phi_K(\vec{x})^4 : d\vec{x} - \frac{1}{2}\delta m^2 \int_{\substack{V \\ t=0}} : \phi_K(\vec{x})^2 : d\vec{x}.$$

Here the cut-off field $\phi_K(x)$ is defined by

$$\phi_K(\vec{x}) = \left(\frac{1}{2V}\right)^{\frac{1}{2}} \sum_{\vec{k}} [a(\vec{k})\, e^{i\vec{k}\vec{x}} + a^*(\vec{k})\, e^{-i\vec{k}\vec{x}}]\, \omega(\vec{k})^{-\frac{1}{2}} \hat{\chi}_K(\vec{k}),$$

where

$$\hat{\chi}_K(\vec{k}) = \begin{cases} 1, & \text{if all the } |k_j| \le K \\ 0, & \text{if some } |k_j| > K. \end{cases}$$

2. Essential Self-Adjointness of the Hamiltonian

Let D_0 be the domain got by applying finite polynominals in the creation operators $a^*(\vec{k})$ to the Fock vacuum Φ_0. The expression H_K can be given a meaning on D_0 as a symmetric operator

$$(H_K | D_0) \subset (H_K | D_0)^*.$$

Furthermore, H_K is essentially self-adjoint on D_0. That is, we can prove

Theorem 1.

$$(H_K | D_0)^{**} = (H_K | D_0)^* = \overline{(H_K | D_0)}.$$

Proof: The operator H_K is bounded below on D_0, so there is a constant α such that $H_K + \alpha$ is strictly positive on D_0. It follows that $(H_K | D_0)$ is essentially self-adjoint if and only if its range is dense in the Hilbert space $\mathscr{H}$. The idea of the proof is to separate off from H_K the part of the Hamiltonian $H^{(1)}$ which involves the degrees of freedom that enter the interaction. Then we shall see from the specific form of $H^{(1)}$ that it can be represented as an elliptic partial differential operator of the form

$$-\Delta + V,$$

where Δ is the Laplacian on R^m and V is multiplication by a polynomial which is bounded below. We can use this property of V along with the regularity theorem for elliptic operators to prove that the range of $H^{(1)} + \alpha$ is dense.

The first step in the proof is to map the Hilbert space $\mathscr{H}$ into a tensor product space

$$\mathscr{H} \rightarrow \hat{\mathscr{H}} = \mathscr{H}_1 \otimes \mathscr{H}_2,$$

and

$$D_0 \rightarrow \hat{D}_0 = D_1 \otimes D_2.$$

The space $\mathscr{H}_1$ is the closure of D_1, where D_1 is generated from Φ_0 by applying polynomials in the creation operators $a^*(\vec{k})$ which enter the interaction Hamiltonian, and, therefore, which are not cut off. The space $\mathscr{H}_2$ is associated in the same manner with the remaining degrees of freedom. Then H_K is mapped into $\hat{H}_K$ of the form

$$\hat{H}_K = H^{(1)} \otimes 1 + 1 \otimes H^{(2)}.$$

Therefore, the essential self-adjointness of $H^{(1)}$ and $H^{(2)}$ can be considered separately.

The operator $H^{(2)}$ acts as the free-field Hamiltonian on $\mathcal{H}_2$. It is essentially self-adjoint on D_2, since D_2 contains a total set of eigenvectors for $H^{(2)}$.

As for the operator $H^{(1)}$, we use coordinates in terms of which it can be written $-\Delta + V$, and these are just, up to multiplicative factors, the even and odd parts of the Fourier coefficients of $\phi_K(x)$ and $\pi_K(x)$, respectively.

$$Q_e(\vec{k}) = [a(\vec{k}) + a^*(\vec{k}) + a(-\vec{k}) + a^*(-\vec{k})]\left[\frac{1}{2\omega(\vec{k})}\right]^{\frac{1}{2}},$$

$$Q_0(\vec{k}) = -i[-a(\vec{k}) + a^*(\vec{k}) + a(-\vec{k}) - a^*(-\vec{k})]\left[\frac{1}{2\omega(\vec{k})}\right]^{\frac{1}{2}},$$

$$P_e(\vec{k}) = \frac{-i}{2}[a(\vec{k}) - a^*(\vec{k}) + a(-\vec{k}) - a^*(-\vec{k})]\left[\frac{\omega(\vec{k})}{2}\right]^{\frac{1}{2}},$$

and

$$P_0(\vec{k}) = \frac{1}{2}[a(\vec{k}) + a^*(\vec{k}) - a(-\vec{k}) - a^*(-\vec{k})]\left[\frac{\omega(\vec{k})}{2}\right]^{\frac{1}{2}}.$$

After the redundant coordinates (under inversion of $\vec{k}$) have been eliminated, the remaining variables satisfy the canonical commutation relations. In terms of these coordinates, the Hilbert space $\mathcal{H}_1$ is represented as $L^2(R^M)$, and the vectors in D_1 are represented as Hermite functions of multiples of the Q variables. Note that these functions are a dense set in $\mathcal{S}(R^M)$. If the range of $H^{(1)} + \alpha$ is not dense, then there exists a nonzero vector ψ in $\mathcal{H}_1$ such that ψ is perpendicular to the range of $H^{(1)} + \alpha$.

$$(H^{(1)} + \alpha)|D_1\}^*\psi = 0.$$

Since D_1 is dense in $\mathcal{S}(R^M)$, and since $H^{(1)}$ is a continuous map of $\mathcal{S}(R^M)$ into $\mathcal{S}(R^M)$, we can identify ψ with a tempered distribution χ which satisfies the equation

$$(H^{(1)} + \alpha)^+\chi = 0.$$

Here $(H^{(1)})^+$ is the distribution adjoint of $H^{(1)}$, and is a continuous map of $\mathcal{S}(R^M)'$ into $\mathcal{S}(R^M)'$. Since $(H^{(1)})^+$ is elliptic partial differential operator with analytic coefficients, it follows from the regularity theorem for elliptic operators that $\chi(Q)$ is a real-analytic function. For example, see reference [4]. Therefore, we can work with

$$(\Delta\chi)(Q) = (V(Q) + \alpha)\chi(Q)$$

as an equation satisfied at each point. Multiplying by $\overline{\chi(Q)}$ gives

$$\frac{1}{2}\Delta|\chi(Q)|^2 = |\nabla\chi(Q)|^2 + \{V(Q) + \alpha\}|\chi(Q)|^2,$$

which is positive if we choose α large enough so that $V + \alpha$ is positive. If we integrate this equation over an M-sphere of radius r, the divergence theorem shows that

$$\int_{\|Q\|^2 \leq r} \Delta|\chi(Q)|^2\, dV = r^{M-1}\frac{\partial}{\partial r}\int_{\|Q\|^2 = r} |\chi(Q)|^2\, d\Omega \geq 0.$$

We then infer that $\chi(Q)$ can not be square integrable, which completes the proof of essential self-adjointness.

It is furthermore possible to prove that the unitary groups generated by $H^{(1)}$ and $H^{(2)}$ commute, so that the dynamics factors on the tensor product. Also H_K has a pure discrete spectrum and the lowest eigenvalue has unit multiplicity.

Theorem 2. For the $\lambda\phi^4$ total Hamiltonian H_K,

1. $\exp(i\hat{H}_K t) = \exp(iH^{(1)}t) \otimes \exp(iH^{(2)}t)$,

and

2. The vacuum state ψ_0 of H_K is nondegenerate.

3. Existence of the Vacuum Expectation Values

We wish to show that Wightman functions exist, and that they are infinitely differentiable in the time. What will be shown is that there exists a dense domain $D_3 \subset \mathscr{H}$ which includes the physical vacuum ψ_0, and which is left invariant by

1. the unitary group $\exp(iH_K t)$,
2. the fields $\phi(f)$ and $\pi(f)$ at $t = 0$,
3. H_K,

and, therefore, by

4. the closure of $\phi(f, t)$ and by all its time derivatives.

Since the dynamics factors on the tensor product space $\mathscr{H}_1 \otimes \mathscr{H}_2$, it is sufficient to prove the desired theorem on each Hilbert space $\mathscr{H}_1$ and $\mathscr{H}_2$. The proof for $\mathscr{H}_2$ is trivial, since the result follows from the well-known behavior of the free-field vacuum expectation values [12]. The domain in question will be D_2, which is just the image in $\mathscr{H}_2$ of D_0.

The idea of the proof on $\mathscr{H}_1$ is to show that three spaces are equal. We shall see that

$$\bigcap_{\vec{k}, n, \pm} D([a(\vec{k}) \pm a^*(\vec{k})]^n) = \bigcap_{n=0}^{\infty} D(H^{(1)n}), \tag{4}$$

and that in terms of the coordinates $Q_e(\vec{k})$ and $Q_0(\vec{k})$ introduced earlier, this domain is just the Schwartz space $\mathcal{S}(R^M(Q))$. Once this fact has been established, it is clear that the fields $\phi_K(f)$ and $\pi_K(f)$ leave the left-hand side of Equation 4 invariant. Furthermore, it is clear that $H^{(1)}$ and $\exp(iH^{(1)}t)$ leave the right side invariant, since $H^{(1)}$ is essentially self-adjoint on this domain. Therefore, in terms of the coordinates Q, the domain $\mathcal{S}(R^M) \subset \mathscr{H}_1$ will serve as the desired invariant domain in $\mathscr{H}_1$.

The proof that Equation 4 holds and that it equals $\mathcal{S}(R^M)$ is lengthy and will not be described here. However, the important step is to demonstrate that two families of norms defined on D_1 give to D_1 the same topology. We have, for example, the norms

$$\|\psi\|_n = \|\phi(f)^{2n}\psi\| + \|\pi(f)^{2n}\psi\| + \|\psi\|$$

and the norms

$$|||\psi|||_n = \|(H^{(1)} + \alpha)^n\psi\|.$$

It is possible to show that for each n and each square integrable f, there is a constant c(n, f) such that for all ψ in D_1,

$$\|\psi\|_n < c(n, f)(|||\psi|||_0 + |||\psi|||_n).$$

The idea of proving these majorizations is to immediately transform to the coordinates in which $H^{(1)}$ becomes $-\Delta + V(Q)$. Then, expand $(H^{(1)} + \alpha)^n$ in terms of $-\Delta$ and $(V + \alpha)$. The contributions $(-\Delta)^n\psi$ and $(V + \alpha)^n\psi$ will majorize $\|\psi\|_n$, if c is sufficiently large.

Thus we must deal with the $2^n - 2$ remaining terms. We extract from each term a positive contribution, which can be neglected, and the remainder terms which is left over can be majorized by $d(|||\psi|||_0 + |||\psi|||_{n-1})$. The proof of this last step will involve a lengthy induction argument. The relevent positive terms will always be separated by using double commutator identies.

As an example of how the simplest majorization can be derived, let us consider an operator B such that

$$B = -\Delta + V(Q),$$

where

$$V(Q) \geq 1.$$

The polynomials $V(Q)$ which arise from $H^{(1)}$ have the additional property that any partial derivative with respect to the Q variables $V_r(Q)$, satisfies the following majorization

$$|V_r(Q)| \leq c(V(Q) + d),$$

where c and d are constants. We will show that this can be used to derive that

$$\|V\psi\|^2 + \|\Delta\psi\|^2 \leq a\|B\psi\|^2 + b\|\psi\|^2.$$

This follows from the fact that

$$(\psi, B^2\psi) = \left(\psi, \left\{\Delta^2 + V^2 + 2\sum_{\substack{j=e,0 \\ \vec{k}}} P_j(\vec{k})VP_j(\vec{k})\right\}\psi\right) + \sum_{\substack{j=e,0 \\ \vec{k}}} (\psi, [P_j(\vec{k}), [P_j(\vec{k}), V]]$$

$$= \|\Delta\psi\|^2 + \|V\psi\|^2 + 2\sum_{\substack{j=e,0 \\ \vec{k}}} \|V^{\frac{1}{2}}P_j(\vec{k})\psi\|^2 - (\psi, (\Delta V)\psi).$$

Therefore, since

$$|(\psi, (\Delta V)\psi)| < c|(\psi, V\psi)| + d|(\psi,\psi)| < c(\psi, B\psi) + d(\psi,\psi),$$

we see that

$$\|\Delta\psi\|^2 + \|V\psi\|^2 < \|B\psi\|^2 + c(\psi, B\psi) + d(\psi,\psi),$$

from which the desired inequality follows by using the spectral theorem. We can summarize the above discussion by

Theorem 3. A dense domain D_3 exists which includes the vacuum ψ and is included in the domain of the closure of $\phi(f, t)$ and any of its time derivatives. It is left invariant by each of these operators. Therefore, the vacuum expectation values and the Green's functions exist for the approximate $\lambda\phi^4$ theory.

4. Properties of the Solutions

We have the following immediate results in the $\lambda\phi^4$ theory. First, $\pi(f, t)$ is the time derivative of $\phi(f, t)$, and the canonical commutation relations are valid at all times.

Theorem 4. For any vector ψ in D_3,

$$1. \quad \pi(f, t)\psi = \exp(iH_K t)\pi(f)\exp(-iH_K t)\psi = \frac{d}{dt}\{\phi(f, t)\psi\},$$

and

$$2. \quad [\pi(f, t), \phi(g, t)]\psi = -i(f, g)\psi,$$

where

$$(f, g) = \int_V f(\vec{x})g(\vec{x})\, d\vec{x}.$$

Second, the vacuum expectation values satisfy equations of motion.

Theorem 5. As distribution equations,

$$(\Box_x + \mu^2)(\psi_0, \phi(\vec{x}, t)\phi(x_1, t_1), \cdots, \phi(\vec{x}_n, t_n)\psi_0)$$

$$= (\psi_0, J(\vec{x}, t)\phi(\vec{x}_1, t_1), \cdots, \phi(\vec{x}_n, t_n)\psi_0),$$

where

$$J(\vec{x}, t) \equiv \exp(iH_K t)J(\vec{x})\exp(-iH_K t),$$

$$J(\vec{x}) = -4\lambda \int_V d\vec{y}_1 \cdots d\vec{y}_4\, K_4(\vec{x}; \vec{y}_1, \cdots, \vec{y}_4) : \phi(\vec{y}_1) \cdots \phi(\vec{y}_4) :$$

$$+ \delta m^2 \int_V d\vec{y}_1\, d\vec{y}_2\, K_2(\vec{x}; \vec{y}_1, \vec{y}_2) : \phi(\vec{y}_1)\phi(\vec{y}_2) : ,$$

$$K_4(\vec{x}; \vec{y}_1, \ldots, \vec{y}_4) = \int_V \chi_K(\vec{y} - \vec{x})\chi_K(\vec{y} - \vec{y}_1) \cdots \chi_K(\vec{y} - \vec{y}_4)\, d\vec{y},$$

and

$$K_2(\vec{x}; \vec{y}_1, \vec{y}_2) = \int_V \chi_K(\vec{y} - \vec{x})\chi_K(\vec{y} - \vec{y}_1)\chi_K(\vec{y} - \vec{y}_2)\, d\vec{y}.$$

In the formal limit $K \to \infty$, $\chi_K(x) \to \delta(\vec{x})$, and

$$K_n(\vec{x}, \vec{y}_1, \ldots, \vec{y}_n) \to \prod_{j=1}^{n} \delta(\vec{x} - \vec{y}_j).$$

From Theorems 4 and 5 we can deduce that the Green's functions also satisfy nonlinear equations of motion.

Theorem 6. Using 4-vector notation with x standing for $(\vec{x}, t)$, we have

$$(\Box_x + m^2)(\psi_0, T\phi(x)\phi(x_1) \cdots \phi(x_n)\psi_0)$$
$$= -i \sum_{j=1}^{n} \delta(x - x_j)(\psi_0, T\phi(x_1) \cdots \widehat{\phi(x_j)} \cdots \phi(x_n)\psi_0)$$
$$+ (\psi_0, TJ(x)\phi(x_1) \cdots \phi(x_n)\psi_0).$$

Remark: The preceding equations of motion are exactly those equations which would result formally from varying the cut-off Lagrangian

$$\mathscr{L}(t) = e^{iH_K t} (\mathscr{L}_0 + \mathscr{L}_I)\, e^{-iH_K t},$$

where $\mathscr{L}_0$ is the free-field Lagrangian, and $\mathscr{L}_I = -H_I$ is the cut-off interaction Lagrangian. Then for ψ in D_3, we have formally

$$(\Box + m^2)\phi(\vec{x}, t)\psi = \exp(iH_K t) \frac{\delta \mathscr{L}_I}{\delta\phi(\vec{x})} \exp(-iH_K t)\psi.$$

Theorem 7. The vacuum expectation values for the $\lambda\phi^4$ theory are not analytic in λ at $\lambda = 0$. However, the vacuum state $\psi_0(\lambda)$ and the resolvent of the Hamiltonian

$$\{Z + H_K(\lambda)\}^{-1}$$

are vector-valued functions of λ which are analytic in the neighborhood of any point λ which is real and positive.

5. The $\lambda\phi^3$ Theory

If one tries to apply the same cut-off method to the $\lambda\phi^3$ theory, trouble will be encountered. While this theory is often studied, it is physically objectionable since the total energy is formally unbounded below.

Let us assume that we have a $\lambda\phi^3$ theory, cut-off as explained earlier, and in which the total probability is conserved in time. Therefore, the time translations form a unitary group $\exp(iH_K t)$, and the infinitesimal generator iH_K is skew-adjoint.

However, a physical argument due to Wightman [10] indicates that the cut-off, $\lambda\phi^3$ total Hamiltonian is not essentially self-adjoint on D_0, the domain on which the $\lambda\phi^4$ Hamiltonian is essentially self-adjoint. Let us assume that this is the case, and we also assume that the dynamics factors on $\mathscr{H}_1 \otimes \mathscr{H}_2$. Then we can prove the following:

Theorem 8. Let ψ be a cyclic vector for the polynomials in the smeared field operators $\phi(f)$ and $\pi(g)$, taken at $t = 0$. Then under the previous assumptions the expectation values in ψ

$$(\psi, \phi(f_1, t_1) \cdots \phi(f_n, t_n)\psi)$$

do not exist for all n and for all $t_1, \cdots, t_n$ in any cube of finite volume,

$$|t_j| < T, \qquad T > 0.$$

Proof: The main steps in the proof we can outline as follows: Since ψ is cyclic for the polynomials in the fields at $t = 0$, it is possible to deduce that ψ is in D_3. However, if all the required expectations values did exist, and if the dynamics does factor, then we can infer that $\exp(iH^{(1)}t)$ maps a dense subset of D_3 into the domain of $H^{(1)}$. From this it is possible to deduce that $H^{(1)}|_{D_0}$ are essentially self-adjoint, a result contrary to assumption.

This trouble in the quantum $\lambda\phi^3$ theory is analogous to a difficulty in the classical $\lambda\phi^3$ theory. Keller [7] starts from the fact that the classical $\lambda\phi^3$ energy integral is unbounded below. He then reasons to show that given a large class of smooth initial data, the corresponding solution $\phi(\vec{x}, t)$ to the equation

$$(\Box + \mu^2)\phi(\vec{x}, t) = -\lambda\phi^2(\vec{x}, t),$$

develops a singularity in a finite time interval. On the other hand global solutions do exist for the classical equation

$$(\Box + \mu^2)\phi(\vec{x}, t) = -\lambda\phi^3(\vec{x}, t).$$

See references [2, 6, 8]. The singularities which occur in the clas sical function $\phi(\vec{x}, t)$ have their counterpart in the singularities wh develop in the quantum mechanical expectation values $(\psi, \phi(\vec{x}_1, t_1) \cdot \phi(\vec{x}_n, t_n)\psi)$. These result from the unboundedness below of the tota $\lambda\phi^3$ Hamiltonian operator in the cut-off theory.

6. Removal of the Cutoff

The reason that we are interested in the vacuum expectation values and the Green's functions, rather than the cut-off Hamiltonian and the corresponding fields themselves, stems from an interest in whether it is possible to remove the cutoff. In this manner we would like to recover a relativistic field theory from the solution of our approximate field theory as the cutoff disappears. We cannot expect that the Hamiltonian, or any eigenstate of the Hamiltonian, will converge to a limit as the cutoff is removed. The reason is that the approximate field operators and the approximate Hamiltonian exist as unbounded operators in the interaction picture Fock space. If a limiting field exists, then Haag's theorem [3] tells us that it will always be realized in a representation of the canonical commutation relations which is unitarily inequivalent to the approximate theory. This fact shows that all the corresponding operators and vectors will not converg

On the other hand, there is no a priori reason why the vacuum expectation values cannot converge as the cutoff is removed, to a limiting set of distributions. The approximate vacuum expectation values satisfy the positive definiteness condition at every step of the limiting procedure, since they are always constructed from vectors and operators. Hence if the vacuum expectation values do converge, the limiting distributions will satisfy the positive definiteness condition. Then it is possible to use Wightman's reconstruction theorem [9] to build up a separable Hilbert space and a field operator on this space corresponding to the interacting field with the cutoff removed. The Hilbert space will have a cyclic vector for the polynominal algebra of smeared fiel operators, and the expectation value of products of fields in this vector will be given by the limiting set of Wightman functions.

As an indication of what may happen in general, we test out ou method on a quadratic interaction Hamiltonian. Even for a quadratic interaction, the interaction must be cut-off in order for it exist as a bona fide operator in Fock space.

It is possible to take, for example, two interacting fields ϕ_1 and ϕ_2 with masses μ_1 and μ_2, respectively, and couple them wi the formal interaction Hamiltonian density $g\phi_1\phi_2$. The Hamiltonian H_K will be given by

$$H_K = H_{0\mu_1} + H_{0\mu_2} + g \int_V \phi_{1K}(\vec{x})\phi_{2K}(\vec{x})\, d\vec{x}.$$

We can solve for the eigenstates of H_K explicitly, compute all the physical vacuum expectation values of the approximate Hamiltonian, and then show that the vacuum expectation values actually do converge as the cutoff is removed. We can reconstruct the limiting theory, and we find that it is exactly the one which we expected from solving directly the equations of motion which formally follow from our "limiting Hamiltonian."

$$(\Box + \mu_1^2)\psi_1 = -g\psi_2$$

$$(\Box + \mu_2^2)\psi_2 = -g\psi_1$$

The Hilbert space of the limiting theory realizes a unitarily inequivalent representation of the canonical, equal-time commutation relations. Thus, neither the Hamiltonian nor the energy eigenstates of the approximate theory have limits as the cutoff is removed. (However, it is interesting to note that in space-time of dimension four or less, but not in higher dimensions, such limits do exist in the $g\phi_1\phi_2$ theory when $K \to \infty$, keeping the volume V fixed.) Hence in the case of a quadratic interaction the method we use is justified; the limiting relativistic theory is recovered from the limiting Wightman functions.

References

1. Araki, H, J. Math. Phys., 1, 492-504 (1960).
2. Browder, F. E., Math. Z., 80, 249-264 (1962).
3. Haag, R., Kgl. Danske Videnskab. Selskab, Mat.-Fys. Medd., 29, No. 12 (1955).
4. Hörmander, L., Linear Partial Differential Equations, Springer-Verlag, Berlin, 1964.
5. Jaffe, A. M., Comm. Math. Phys., 1, 127-149 (1965).
6. Jörgens, K., Math. Zeit., 77, 299-308 (1961).
7. Keller, J. B., Comm. Pure App. Maths., 10, 523-530 (1957).
8. Segal, I., Ann. Math., 78, 339-364 (1963).
9. Wightman, A. S., Phys. Rev., 101, 860-866 (1956).

10. Wightman, A. S., "An Introduction to the Relativistic Dynamics of Quantized Fields," in Proceedings of the 1964 Cargèse Summer School, ed. M. Lévy, Gordon & Breach, New York, 1966.

11. Wightman, A. S., and L. Gårding, Proc. Nat. Acad. Sci. U.S., 40, 622-626 (1954).

12. Wightman, A. S., and L. Gårding, "Fields as Operator Valued Distributions," Arkiv Fysik, 28, 129-184 (1964).

13. Wightman, A. S., and S. S. Schweber, Phys. Rev., 98, 813-837 (1955).

Chapter 5

ON THE CALCULATION OF SOME HOLOMORPHY ENVELOPES OF INTEREST IN PHYSICS

Gunnar Källén

The basic quantity which we are going to consider is the vacuum expectation value of a time-ordered product of n-scalar Hermitian field operators $A_i(x_i)$. As is well known, this function is the boundary value of an analytic function, both in x-space and in p-space. More explicitly, we introduce the notation

$$\langle 0|T(A_1(x_1) \cdots A_n(x_n))|0\rangle$$

$$= F_n(x) = \frac{1}{(2\pi)^{4n-4}} \int \cdots \int \prod_{j=1}^{n-1} dp_j \exp\left[i \sum_{j=1}^{n-1} p_j(x_j - x_{j+1}) \right] H_n(p), \tag{1}$$

$$F_n(x) = \text{B.V. } F_n(z), \tag{1a}$$

$$H_n(p) = \text{B.V. } H_n(\widetilde{z}), \tag{1b}$$

where the sympol T stands for time ordering and B.V. means boundary value. Further, the letters x and p in the arguments of the functions $F_n(x)$ and $H_n(p)$ is a shorthand notation for all the vectors involved. The complex numbers z and $\widetilde{z}$ in Equations 1a and 1b correspond to the scalar products between the vectors. Actually they are $(n - 1) \times (n - 1)$ matrices related to the scalar products in the following way:

$$\mathrm{Re}(z_{jk}) = -\zeta_j\zeta_k = (\zeta_j)_0(\zeta_k)_0 - \overline{\zeta}_j\overline{\zeta}_k, \tag{2a}$$

$$\mathrm{Re}(\widetilde{z}_{jk}) = -p_jp_k = (p_j)_0(p_k)_0 - \overline{p}_j\overline{p}_k, \tag{2b}$$

$$\zeta_j = x_j - x_{j+1}. \tag{2c}$$

The boundary values appearing in Equations 1a and 1b are taken in such a way that the imaginary parts of the variables z are infinitesimal and negative while the imaginary parts of the variables $\tilde{z}$ are infinitesimal and positive.

We are here mainly interested in the analyticity domains of the functions $F_n(z)$ and $H_n(\tilde{z})$. As is well known, it follows from standard assumptions about Lorentz invariance, local commutativity, and reasonable mass spectrum that the function $F_n(z)$ has a representation of the form

$$F_n(z) = \int_0^\infty \cdots \int_0^\infty \prod_{j\leq k=1}^{n-1} da_{jk}\, \Delta_n^{(+)}(z;a) G_n(a), \tag{3}$$

$$\Delta_n^{(+)}(z;a) = \frac{1}{(2\pi)^{3n-3}} \int \cdots \int \prod_{j=1}^{n-1} dp_j \exp\left(i \sum_{j=1}^{n-1} p_j \zeta_j\right)$$

$$\times \prod_{j\leq k=1}^{n-1} \delta(p_j p_k + a_{jk}) \prod_{\ell=1}^{n-1} \theta(p_\ell), \tag{3a}$$

where the function $G_n(a)$ is essentially the Fourier transform of the non-time-ordered product of the same operators that appear on the left-hand side of Equation 1. There is one representation, Equation 3, for each way in which the n operators can be multiplied together. Clearly, the function $G_n(a)$ is related to the function $H_n(p)$, but they are not identical. Actually, there exists a certain algebraic rule according to which $G_n(a)$ can be expressed in terms of different boundary values of the function $H_n(z)$. However, this rule is immaterial for our discussion here, and we shall not go into detail.

The integrals in Equation 3a can be worked out, and the analyticity domain of the kernel function $\Delta_n^{(+)}(z;a)$ can be exhibited explicitly. The result is conveniently expressed in terms of the eigenvalues of the matrix $M = za$. Denoting the eigenvalues of this matrix by σ_j, we find that the kernel $\Delta_n^{(+)}(z;a)$ does not decrease exponentially for large values of the "masses" a_{jk} as soon as any condition of the form

$$\operatorname{Im}\left(\sum_{j=1}^{n-1} \pm \sqrt{\sigma_j}\right) = 0 \tag{4}$$

is fulfilled. Consequently, the integration over the masses a, in Equation 3, is not convergent when Equation 4 holds, except for very special behaviors of the functions $G_n(a)$, and one must, in general, expect the function $F_n(z)$ to have singularities. However, for each representation, Equation 3, there is a certain domain in the scalar variables z where the function $F_n(z)$ is regular and the boundary of this regularity domain is determined by Equation 4. After some algebraic manipulations, the matrix determining this boundary can be written in the following parametric form:

$$z = \alpha a \alpha. \tag{5}$$

(An equivalent expression was originally given by R. Jost.) Here, quantities α and a are symmetric matrices fulfilling the relations

$$\alpha = \alpha^T, \tag{6a}$$

$$\mathrm{Im}\, \alpha_{jk} = 0, \qquad j \neq k, \tag{6b}$$

$$\mathrm{Im}\, \alpha_{jj} > 0, \tag{6c}$$

$$a_{jj} = 0, \tag{7a}$$

and

$$a_{jk} = a_{kj} > 0, \qquad j \neq k. \tag{7b}$$

The two matrices α and a are $(m \times m)$ matrices with $m \leq n$. In the case where $m < n$, the matrix z defined by Equation 5 is smaller than the matrix z appearing in Equation 3. In that case, those complex numbers z which do not appear in Equation 5 are arbitrary in Equation 3. One can show that the surfaces defined in this way have exactly the right dimension to be boundary surfaces of a regularity domain in the space of the complex variables z. The analyticity domain is the intersection of the domains defined by all these surfaces with $m \leq n$ and such that the case when all the variables z are negative and real is inside the domain.

Clearly, the domain indicated in Equations 5 through 7 is rather complicated. Because of the way it has been defined through the representation of Equation 3, each domain is evidently a natural domain of holomorphy. However, for each function $F_n(z)$ there are, as has already been mentioned, several representations of the form of Equation 5 corresponding to the different ways in which the operators appearing on the left-hand side of Equation 1 can be multiplied together. Each one of these representations implies that the function $F_n(z)$ is regular in a separate domain and, therefore, the function $F_n(z)$ is regular in the union of all these domains. As this union is normally not a natural domain of holomorphy, we are faced with the problem of calculating the holomorphy envelope of the union of the domains defined here. The ultimate goal once this holomorphy envelope is known would be to find a representation for the most general function regular and analytic in this holomorphy envelope. Evidently, we are very far from that goal as of today. The only nontrivial case where the holomorphy envelope has been explicitly constructed is the case $n = 3$. (The case $n = 2$ is trivial and does not concern us here.) In that case it turns out that an important part of the boundary of the holomorphy envelope is given by a curve very similar to Equation 5 but with the equation

$$z = -\alpha a \alpha. \tag{8}$$

The proof of this statement is somewhat special [1, 2] and works only for the case $n = 3$. Essentially, it consists of a series of mappings where the domain defined by Equations 5 through 7 is mapped on a tube domain. Afterwards, the calculation of the holomorphy envelope is trivial. However, the mapping technique can easily be shown not to work for $n \geq 4$. Nevertheless, the strong analogy between Equations 5 and 8 is very striking and suggests that even if the method of proof cannot be generalized, the result may still have some validity also for larger values of n. This idea has been considerably strengthened recently since A. C. Wu [3] has been able to show that the so-called "Landau singularity" of a certain class of Feynman diagrams corresponding to the perturbation theory expression for the functions $F_n(z)$ has a branch which is exactly of the structure of Equation 8. Therefore, it is reasonable to expect that the domain bounded by these curves at least gives an upper bound for the unknown holomorphy envelope. (To make the argument conclusive it would be necessary to show that this Landau singularity lies on the physica sheet and that no other singularity appears earlier. These points have not yet been cleared up.)

In view of the situation just outlined, we are looking for a systematic technique which would not be so intimately connected with the special features of the case $n = 3$ as the methods used until now and which exploits the close analogy between the expected answer, Equation 8, and the starting point, Equation 5. I should like to outline one attempt in this direction which is base on ideas produced by A. C. Wu, J. Islam, H. Lam, and the auth To illustrate the idea, I treat explicitly the case $n = 3$, where th answer is already known. However, the main point of the argum is evidently that it looks as if the essential steps could be carried through for all values of n. The starting point is the remark that it is possible to distort the contours of integration for the time components of the vectors in Equation 3 and to write the Fourier transform connecting the functions $F_n(x)$ and $H_n(p)$ as a four-dimensional Euclidean Fourier transform. In terms of the scalar variables z, this technique implies that we restrict ourselves to a domain where the diagonal values z_{jj} are both negative and where the inequality

$$-\sqrt{z_{11}z_{22}} \leq z_{12} \leq \sqrt{z_{11}z_{22}} \tag{9}$$

is fulfilled. Let us denote this domain by D. Using the invariance of both the functions F_n and H_n, it is possible to integrate over all angles and write a formula similar to Equation 3:

$$F_3(z) = \int_{\tilde{z}\in D} E(z;\tilde{z})H_3(\tilde{z})\, d\tilde{z}, \qquad z \in D, \tag{10}$$

$$E(z;\tilde{z}) = \frac{1}{(2\pi)^8} \iint d^4p\, d^4p'\, \delta(p^2 + \tilde{z}_{11})\delta(p'^2 + \tilde{z}_{22})$$

$$\times\, \delta(pp' + \tilde{z}_{12}) \exp\,[i(p\zeta_1 + p'\zeta_2)]$$

$$= -\frac{1}{(2\pi)^6} \frac{1}{2\sqrt{z_{11}z_{22} - z_{12}^2}} [J_0(\sqrt{Q + \sqrt{R}}) - J_0(\sqrt{Q - \sqrt{R}})], \tag{10a}$$

$$Q = z_{11}\tilde{z}_{11} + z_{22}\tilde{z}_{22} + 2z_{12}\tilde{z}_{12} = \mathrm{Sp}[z\tilde{z}], \tag{10b}$$

$$R = 4(z_{11}z_{22} - z_{12}^2)(\tilde{z}_{11}\tilde{z}_{22} - \tilde{z}_{12}^2) = 4\, \mathrm{Det}|z|\, \mathrm{Det}|\tilde{z}|. \tag{10c}$$

The representation given in Equation 10 is true only when both the points z and $\tilde{z}$ belong to the domain D. However, the function $H_3(\tilde{z})$ is regular in the same domain as the function $F_3(z)$ [1, 2]. As the kernel $E(z;\tilde{z})$ is also analytic as function of both z and $\tilde{z}$, it is, in principle, possible to continue the function $F_3(z)$ analytically. For this purpose it is convenient to be able to modify the path of integration, thereby exploiting the analyticity properties of the integrand. The general idea is to take advantage of the analyticity of $H_3(\tilde{z})$ only in the union of the domains defined by Equations 5 through 7, and try to see if this is enough to continue the function $F_3(z)$ to the holomorphy envelope. Actually, Equation 10 is not very well suited for such a program because the kernel function $E(z;\tilde{z})$ is exponentially increasing in practically all directions in the space of the complex variables $\tilde{z}$. Therefore, nearly any modification of the path of integration in Equation 10 will yield a divergent integral unless the function $H_3(\tilde{z})$ is supposed to decrease very rapidly at infinity. However, such a decrease is physically unreasonable. We can remedy this defect of the representation Equation 10 by using a Cauchy representation for the function $H_3(\tilde{z})$:

$$H_3(\tilde{z}) = \frac{1}{(2\pi i)^3} \int_C \frac{dt\, H_3(t)}{\Pi(t - \tilde{z})}. \tag{11}$$

The path C in Equation 11 can, for example, be chosen to be a "product" of three paths, one in each of the planes of the variables $\tilde{z}_{jk}$. Further, the path has to encircle all points inside the domain D. A possible path that does this would start at $-\infty$ below the negative real axis, continue up to the origin, encircle this point in a positive sense, and return above the negative real axis. (At this point it is necessary to make the technical assumption that the mass spectrum of the theory does not extend the whole way to zero. Under those circumstances, there is a small part of the positive real axis which belongs to the regularity domain of the function $H_3(t)$. Therefore, the path C can be as indicated. This is also the reason why it is convenient to write Equation 10 in the given form and not with the roles of the functions $H_3(\tilde{z})$ and $F_3(z)$ reversed.) In this way we get

$$F_3(z) = \frac{1}{(2\pi i)^3} \int_C dt\, h(z;t) H_3(t), \qquad z \in D, \tag{12}$$

$$h(z;t) = \int_{\tilde{z}\in D} \frac{E(z;\tilde{z})}{\Pi(t - \tilde{z})}\, d\tilde{z}. \tag{12a}$$

The integration exhibited in Equation 12a can be simplified to a considerable extent, and all three complex integrations can be expressed in terms of one single real integral. The result is

$$h(z;t) = \frac{1}{4} \frac{1}{(2\pi)^4} \int_0^\infty \frac{ds\, J_0(\sqrt{s})}{(s + Q)^2 - R} L(z;t;s). \tag{13}$$

The two symbols Q and R in Equation 13 are quantities analogous to those exhibited in Equations 10b and 10c but with the matrix $\tilde{z}$ replaced by the matrix t. The last factor L(z;t;s) is a certain logarithm. Its explicit form is not very interesting for our argument here but, for completeness, we record it. For this purpose it is convenient to introduce the three variables z_1, z_2, and z_3 according to the definitions

$$z_1 = z_{11}, \tag{14a}$$

$$z_2 = z_{22}, \tag{14b}$$

$$z_3 = z_{11} + z_{22} + 2z_{12}, \tag{14c}$$

and also the corresponding variables instead of the matrix t, with the sign of term $2t_{12}$ in the definition of t_3 reversed as compared to Equation 14c. This gives

$$L(z;t;s) = \sum_{j=1}^{3} \frac{\partial D}{\partial z_j} \frac{1}{\sqrt{\lambda_{k\ell}}} \log X_{k\ell}, \tag{15}$$

$$D = (s + Q)^2 - R, \tag{15a}$$

$$\lambda_{k\ell} = (s - t_k z_\ell - t_\ell z_k)^2 - 4z_k z_\ell t_k t_\ell, \tag{15b}$$

$$X_{k\ell} = \frac{s - t_k z_\ell - t_\ell z_k - \sqrt{\lambda_{k\ell}}}{s - t_k z_\ell - t_\ell z_k + \sqrt{\lambda_{k\ell}}}. \tag{15c}$$

The only feature of the function L(z;t;s) worth noting here is the fact that on the manifold $D = 0$ it reduces to

$$L(z;t;s)\big|_{D=0} = 2\sqrt{t_{11}t_{22} - t_{12}^2}\, \log (1)$$

$$= 4ni\pi \sqrt{t_{11}t_{22} - t_{12}^2}. \tag{16}$$

Therefore, the singularity appearing in Equation 13 when the denominator vanishes is sometimes canceled by a corresponding zero in the function L(z;t;s). Further, it should be noted that the function h(z;t) is similar to a Hankel function and does not have the exponential increase in most directions implied by the

Bessel functions in Equation 10a. Finally, it might be mentioned that h(z;a) is the x-space function belonging to the particular diagram shown in Figure 1. The algebraic structure of the kernels

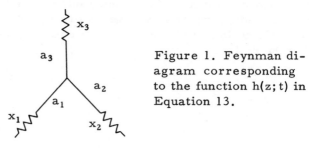

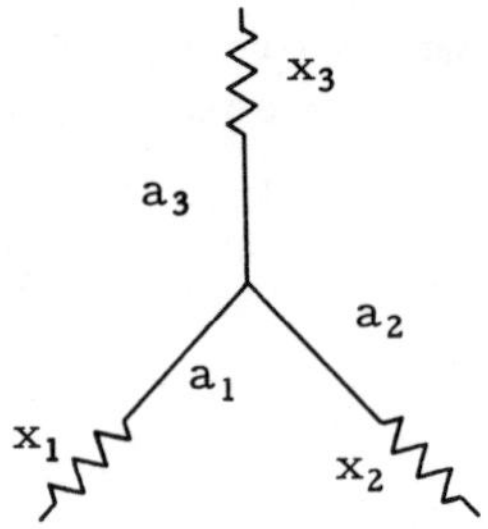

Figure 1. Feynman diagram corresponding to the function h(z; t) in Equation 13.

h(z;t) in Equation 13 is very similar to the structure of the function $\Delta_3^{(+)}(z;a)$ in Equation 3a. Actually, we have

$$\Delta_3^{(+)}(z;a) = \frac{i}{(4\pi)^2} \frac{1}{\sqrt{z_{12}^2 - z_{11}z_{22}}} \left[H_0^{(1)}(\sqrt{Q + \sqrt{R}}) - H_0^{(1)}(\sqrt{Q - \sqrt{R}})\right]$$

$$= \frac{1}{(2\pi)^4} \sqrt{a_{12}^2 - a_{11}a_{22}} \int_0^\infty \frac{ds\, J_0(\sqrt{s})}{(s - Q)^2 - R}. \quad (17)$$

In this case the quantities Q and R are constructed from the matrices z and a. We note that the denominator in Equation 17 has a structure which is very similar to the denominator in Equation 13. The only difference is a sign difference which can, for example, be so formulated that all the variables z are replaced by -z when one goes from the denominator in Equation 13 to the corresponding expression in Equation 17. Further, it might be mentioned that the vanishing of the denominator in Equation 17 corresponds to the condition stated in Equation 4 and which implies the singularity manifold, Equation 5. Therefore, it would follow immediately that the vanishing of the denominator in Equation 13 implies the singularity manifold, Equation 8, if it were not for the fact that the variables t in Equation 13 are negative instead of positive. However, if the integrand in Equation 12 is such that at least parts of the contour C can be deformed from the negative to the positive real axes, it would be possible to combine the function $F_3(z)$ from the domain $z \in D$ and into a domain bounded by the manifold Equation 8. This manifold, on the other hand, is an important part of the boundary of the known holomorph envelope for the case n = 3. (From this point of view, the main mission of the logarithm L(z;t;s) is to delete some parts of the singularity manifold, Equation 8 which are not relevant.) Finally, we should like to mention that the algebraic structure of the formalism given here is essentially independent of the value of n. Therefore, there is good hope that a similar argument can be carried through also for the general n point function.

To make the ideas just sketched into a reasonably consistent argument it is necessary to carry through a detailed "pinching" argument in the representation Equation 12 exploiting the coincidence of singularities in the kernel h(z;t) and in the function $H_3(t)$. All the algebraic details of such an argument have not been carried through yet. Probably it would be too much to try even to indicate exactly what has been done. However, let us mention one of the important points. When two of the variables t are at the origin and the corresponding paths of integration get pinched between the singularities on the negative real axis from h(z;t) on one side and the singularities on the positive real axis from $H_3(t)$ on the other side, we have a good candidate for a singularity in the function $F_3(z)$. In this situation, the remaining variable t can vary freely in its whole plane cut along the positive real axis. It follows that one important final pinch occurs when two of the variables t are zero and the remaining one positive. This gives exactly the manifold, Equation 8.

The discussion of all possible pinches in the representation, Equation 13, is far from complete yet but, so far, no serious problem has arisen, and we feel that there is hope that the ideas indicated here can be transformed to a reasonably consistent argument. Needless to say, this hope may turn out to be wrong.

References

1. Källén, G., and A. Wightman, Kgl. Danske Videnskab. Selskab, Mat.-Fys. Skrifter, 1, No. 6 (1958).
2. Ruelle, D., Helv. Phys. Acta, 34, 587 (1961).
3. Wu, A. C., Phys. Rev., 135B, 222, 230 (1964).

Chapter 6

A QUARTIC INTERACTION IN TWO DIMENSIONS

Edward Nelson

We consider the neutral scalar field ϕ of mass $\mu > 0$ with free Hamiltonian H_0 and interaction Hamiltonian

$$H_I = g \int : \phi(x)^4 : dx,$$

where $g \geq 0$. In two-dimensional space time, H_I is a well-defined operator if the system is placed in a spatial box with periodic boundary conditions, so that the integration is over a finite interval, say $[0, 2\pi]$. Our result is that the total Hamiltonian $H = H_0 + H_I$ is bounded below, and so has a natural self-adjoint extension (the Friedrichs extension).

This result is a first step toward obtaining the existence of a local relativistic quantum field interaction in two-dimensional space time. In order to do this, it will be necessary to get rid of the box. Suppose that H has a nondegenerate ground state Ψ_0 (the vacuum), and suppose that the results reported to this conference by Arthur Jaffe [3] on the existence of vacuum expectation values extend to this case. One feels that a spatial box does less violence to the dynamics than does an ultraviolet cutoff, so there is some hope that limits of the vacuum expectation values as the box tends to infinity could be shown to exist and have the desired properties (see Reference [6]).

Since we hope that progress will be made on some of these remaining aspects of the problem, a complete account of our result will be postponed. We limit ourselves here to a description of the method.

The proof that H is bounded below is complicated by the fact that the interaction Hamiltonian is neither bounded below (due to the Wick ordering in H_I) nor small compared to H_0 (due to the occurrence of the fourth power in H_I). Therefore we must show that in some sense the negative part of H_I is small compared to H_0. This is accomplished by means of functional integration.

The neutral scalar field may be regarded as an assembly of harmonic oscillators. As in our report to the preceding conference [4],[1] we represent the harmonic oscillator by the Hamiltonian

$$H_\omega = -\left(\frac{1}{2}\frac{d}{dq^2} - \omega q \frac{d}{dq}\right)$$

on L^2 of the line with respect to the Gaussian measure

$$\phi_0^2(q)\,dq = \left(\frac{\omega}{\pi}\right)^{\frac{1}{2}} \exp\left[-\omega q^2\right] dq.$$

Then $-H_\omega$ is the infinitesimal generator of a Markoff process and, for $t > 0$,

$$e^{-tH_\omega}\,\Psi(q) = \int_{-\infty}^{\infty} p^t(q, q')\Psi(q')\varphi_0^2(q')\,dq'$$

for all Ψ in $L^2(\varphi_0^2(q)\,dq)$, where

$$p^t(q, q') = (1 - e^{-2\omega t})^{-\frac{1}{2}} \exp\left[-\frac{\omega(q' - e^{-\omega t}q)^2}{1 - e^{-2\omega t}} + \omega q'^2\right].$$

This is essentially the Abel-Hermite kernel and may be derived from results on Hermite polynomials [2] or from Doob's study [1] of the Langevin equation. Next we evaluate the Gaussian integral

$$a^2 = \int_{-\infty}^{\infty} [p^t(q, q')]^2\varphi_0^2(q')\,dq',$$

obtaining

$$a^2 = (1 - e^{-4\omega t})^{-\frac{1}{2}} \exp\left[\frac{2\omega\, e^{-2\omega t}\, q^2}{1 + e^{-2\omega t}}\right].$$

---

[1] We take this occasion to point out a serious error in the proof of Lemma 15 ([4]; p. 112). The statement that the expectation of any (iterated) stochastic integral is 0 is false. A proof of a stron[ger] result than the theorem of [4] is, however, contained in [5].

By the Schwarz inequality, it follows that

$$|e^{-tH_\omega}\Psi(q)| \leq a\,\|\Psi\|_2,$$

where, for $1 \leq p < \infty$,

$$\|\Psi\|_p^p = \int_{-\infty}^{\infty} |\Psi(q)|^p \varphi_0^2(q)\, dq.$$

Consequently, if $p - 1 < e^{2\omega t}$,

$$\|e^{-tH_\omega}\Psi\|_p \leq (1 - e^{-4\omega t})^{-\frac{1}{4}}\left(1 - \frac{pe^{-2\omega t}}{1 + e^{-2\omega t}}\right)^{-\frac{1}{2p}} \|\Psi\|_2,$$

so that e^{-tH_ω} is a bounded operator from L^2 to L^p, if t is large enough.

We represent Fock space as $\mathscr{H} = L^2(Q, Pr)$, where Q is a Cartesian product of copies of the real line (one for each oscillator), and Pr is the product of the Gaussian probability measures. To discuss the field it is convenient to introduce complex linear combinations q_k of the cosine and sine oscillator coordinates satisfying $q_{-k} = \overline{q}_k$. The q_k, (for $k \geq 0$) are independent Gaussian random variables of mean 0 and variance $1/\omega(k)$ which are complex and isotropic (except for q_0, which is real). In terms of them, the formal expression for the field is (except for a constant factor, which we ignore)

$$\varphi(x) = \sum_{k=-\infty}^{\infty} q_k e^{ikx}.$$

Let

$$:q_{k_1} q_{k_2} q_{k_3} q_{k_4}: = q_{k_1} q_{k_2} q_{k_3} q_{k_4}$$

if $k_i + k_j \neq 0$ for i, j = 1, 2, 3, 4; let

$$:q_{k_1} q_{-k_1} q_{k_2} q_{-k_2}: = \left(q_{k_1} q_{-k_1} - \frac{1}{\omega(k_1)}\right)\left(q_{k_2} q_{-k_2} - \frac{1}{\omega(k_2)}\right)$$

if $k_1 \pm k_2 \neq 0$; and let

$$:q_{k_1} q_{k_1} q_{-k_1} q_{-k_1}: = q_{k_1} q_{k_1} q_{-k_1} q_{-k_1} - \frac{3}{\omega(k_1)^2}.$$

Then H_I is multiplication by gV,

$$V = \Sigma' :q_{k_1} q_{k_2} q_{k_3} q_{k_4}:,$$

where Σ' denotes the summation over all k_1, k_2, k_3, k_4 with sum 0. Since the

$$:q_{k_1} q_{k_2} q_{k_3} q_{k_4}:$$

are orthogonal with square norm

$$[\omega(k_1)\omega(k_2)\omega(k_3)\omega(k_4)]^{-1}, \quad 4[\omega(k_1)\omega(k_2)]^{-2}, \text{ and } 6\omega(k_1)^{-4},$$

respectively, in the three preceding cases, V is a well-defined function in $L^2(Q, Pr)$.

The Feynman-Kac formula asserts that

$$(\Phi, e^{-tH}\Psi) = E\bar{\Phi}(q(0)) \exp\left[-g\int_0^t V(q(s))\,ds\right]\Psi(q(t)),$$

where q(t) is the position of a particle in the Markoff process on Q at time t, and E denotes expectation. Our task is to show that e^{-tH} is a bounded operator on $\mathscr{H}$ and hence that H is bounded below. By the smoothing properties of the Markoff process discussed earlier, if Φ and Ψ are in L^2, then $\bar{\Phi}(q(0))\Psi(q(t))$ (for t sufficiently large) is in L^p for a $p > 1$. Hence it suffices to show that $\exp[-g\int_0^t V(q(s))\,ds]$ is in $L^{p'}$ for $p' < \infty$. The same proof that shows it is in L^1 shows that it is in $L^{p'}$ for all $p' < \infty$. For simplicity of notation, instead of $g\int_0^t V(q(s))\,ds$, we discuss V(q).

Formally, let

$$c = \sum \frac{1}{\omega(k)}.$$

Then

$$:\varphi(x)^4: = \varphi(x)^4 - 6c\varphi(x)^2 + 3c^2 = (\varphi(x)^2 - 3c)^2 - 6c^2,$$

so that V is bounded below by $-6c^2$. Since c is logarithmically infinite, this is of no use as it stands. Define V_κ by taking, in the sum defining V, only k_i with $|k_i| \leq \kappa$, and define c_κ similarly. Then V_κ is bounded below by $-6c_\kappa^2$, which is of the order $\log^2 \kappa$. Define V'_κ by $V = V_\kappa + V'_\kappa$.

Let $x \geq 0$ and let x be of the form $6c_\kappa^2$ for some κ. We wish to estimate $\Pr\{q : V(q) \leq -x - 1\}$. Then this is $\leq \Pr\{q : |V'_\kappa(q)| \geq 1\}$, which is clearly $\leq E(V'_\kappa)^{2j}$ for any positive integer j. Now V'_κ is of degree 4 in Gaussian random variables, and it is easy to derive the estimate

$$E(V'_\kappa)^{2j} \leq \frac{(8j)!}{2^{4j}(4j)!} (EV'^2_\kappa)^j.$$

Next we estimate EV'^2_κ and, using Stirling's formula, choose j to minimize the right-hand side. In this way we obtain the estimate

$$\Pr\{q : V(q) \leq -x - 1\} \leq \exp\left[-c_1 \exp\left(c_2 x^{\frac{1}{2}}\right)\right],$$

where c_1 and c_2 are strictly positive constants. This implies that e^{-V} is integrable.

This completes the outline of the proof that H is bounded below.

Acknowledgments

This work was done while the author was an Alfred P. Sloan Foundation Fellow. The author wishes to thank Professors Res Jost and Markus Fierz for their kind hospitality at the Institüt für Theoretische Physik of the E.T.H. (Zürich).

References

1. Doob, J. L., "The Brownian Movement and Stochastic Equations," Ann. Math., 43, 351-369 (1942).

2. Hille, E., "A Class of Reciprocal Functions," Ann. Math., 27, 427-464 (1926).

3. Jaffe, Arthur M., Dynamics of a Cut-Off $\lambda\phi^4$ Field Theory, Dissertation, Princeton University.

4. Nelson, Edward, "Schrödinger Particles Interacting with a Quantized Scalar Field," Analysis in Function Space, eds. W. T. Martin and I. E. Segal, M.I.T. Press (1964), pp. 87-120.

5. Nelson, Edward, "Interaction of Nonrelativistic Particles with a Quantized Scalar Field," J. Math. Phys., 5, 1190-1197 (1964).

6. Streater, R. F., and A. S. Wightman, PCT, Spin and Statistics, and All That, W. A. Benjamin, Inc., New York (1964).

Chapter 7

A FIELD-THEORY-LIKE AXIOM SYSTEM

David Ruelle

The "main problem"[1] of axiomatic field theory is still to find a nontrivial model satisfying the Wightman axioms. The fact that direct attacks on this problem [5] have failed to solve it does not appear unnatural if one remarks that even for much simpler axiom systems it is hard to write down a nontrivial solution.

I would like now to present one very simple axiom system for which the set of all solutions can be exhibited in a rather intuitive way, although it is hard to write down a really interesting solution in explicit analytic form.

We define a vector space $\mathscr{K}$ as the direct sum over p of the spaces $\mathscr{K}(R^{p\nu})$ of real continuous functions with compact support in $(R^{\nu})^p$. An element f of $\mathscr{K}$ is thus a sequence (f^p) of functions of an increasing number of vector variables in R^{ν}, such that $f^p = 0$ for p sufficiently large. If $f = (f^p)$, $g = (g^p)$ are elements of $\mathscr{K}$, a product $f * g$ is defined by

$$(f * g)^p(x_1, \dots, x_p) = \sum_{j=0}^{p} f^j(x_1, \dots, x_j) g^{p-j}(x_{j+1}, \dots, x_p)$$

so that $\mathscr{K}$ becomes a (noncommutative) algebra with identity 1.

In axiomatic field theory [1] one would instead of real continuous functions with compact support use the space $\mathscr{D}$ or $\mathcal{S}$ of Schwartz, and for every sequence $f = (f^p)$ define a smeared field operator A(f) such that

$$A(f * g) = A(f) \cdot A(g).$$

We introduce now a linear operation Δ in $\mathscr{K}$, the field-theoretical meaning of which will, in our case, be to remove the

[1] See Streater and Wightman [3].

singular part of the Wightman functions which is obtained when two vector arguments coincide.

Let $f \in \mathscr{K}(R^{p\nu})$, $p > 0$, and let ω be a partition of the set $\{1, 2, \cdots, p\}$ into r subsets $S_1 = \{i_{11}, i_{12}, \cdots\}, \cdots, S_r = \{i_{r1}, i_{r2}, \cdots\}$. We may suppose that $i_{jk} < i_{jk'}$ if $k < k'$ and $i_{j1} < i_{j'1}$ if $j < j'$. For all $Y = (y_1, \cdots, y_r) \in R^{r\nu}$, let $x_i^{\omega}(Y) = y_j$ if $i \in S_j$. We define $f_\omega \in \mathscr{K}(R^{r\nu})$ by

$$f_\omega(y_1, \cdots, y_r) = f_\omega(Y) = f(x_1^\omega(Y), \cdots, x_p^\omega(Y)).$$

The sum of the f_ω over all partitions of $\{1, 2, \cdots, p\}$ is an element Δf of $\mathscr{K}$. For $f^0 \in \mathscr{K}(R^0) = R$ we write $\Delta f^0 = f^0$. Then Δ extends by linearity to a linear mapping of $\mathscr{K}$ into itself, which has an inverse Δ^{-1}.

Finally we define a translation τ_a by $a \in R^\nu$ on the elements of $\mathscr{K}$ by

$$(\tau_a f)^p(x_1, \cdots, x_p) = f^p(x_1 - a, \cdots, x_p - a).$$

We are now in position to describe our theory which is a simple commutative field theory consisting in four objects, $\mathscr{H}$, Q, U, Ω, satisfying the following axioms.

$\mathscr{H}$: $\mathscr{H}$ is a complex Hilbert space.

Q : Q is a mapping of $\mathscr{K}$ to self-adjoint operators in $\mathscr{H}$ such that

Q_1. For all $f, g \in \mathscr{K}$ the spectral projections of Q(f), Q(g) commute.

Q_2. Q is a homomorphism in the sense that for all f, $g \in \mathscr{K}$ and for all real scalar λ we have

$$\begin{aligned} Q(1) &= 1 \\ Q(\lambda f) &\supset \lambda Q(f) \\ Q(f + g) &\supset Q(f) + Q(g) \\ Q(f * g) &\supset Q(f) \cdot Q(g). \end{aligned}$$

Q_3. If $0 \leq f \in \mathscr{K}$, then $Q(\Delta^{-1} f) \geq 0$.

U : U is a unitary representation of the additive group R^ν in $\mathscr{H}$ such that

$$U(a)Q(f)U(-a) = Q(\tau_a f)$$

for all $a \in R^\nu$, $f \in \mathscr{K}$.

Ω : Ω is an element of $\mathscr{H}$ such that $\|\Omega\| = 1$ and

Ω_1. For all $a \in T$: $U(a)\Omega = \Omega$.

Ω_2. Ω is cyclic with respect to Q in the sense that if $\mathscr{A} = \{\varphi(Q(f_1), \cdots, Q(f_q)) : q$ natural integer; $f_1, \cdots, f_q \in \mathscr{K}$; φ bounded continuous complex function$\}$ then $\mathscr{A}\Omega$ is dense in $\mathscr{H}$.

I have now to describe what the solutions of this axiom system are. This I shall do in an intuitive rather than precise manner because, in such a brief exposition, technical details would only obscure the picture.

Consider a set E of points in R^ν such that for every compact K, $E \cap K$ is finite. For every $f \in \mathscr{K}$, a real continuous function Sf on R^ν is defined by

$$Sf(y) = \sum_p \sum_{x_1 \in E} \cdots \sum_{x_p \in E} f^p(x_1 - y, \cdots, x_p - y).$$

If the points of the set E are distributed in a sufficiently homogeneous way in R^ν (it is at this point that we fail to be precise), it will be possible to define the distribution of the values of functions $Sf_1, \cdots, Sf_q$. This distribution of values will be a positive measure $\mu_{f_1 \cdots f_q}$ of norm 1 on R^q such that for every bounded complex continuous function φ on R^ν,

$$\mu_{f_1 \cdots f_q}(\varphi) = \mathscr{M}_y \varphi(Sf_1(y), \cdots, Sf_q(y)),$$

where $\mathscr{M}_y$ denotes a supposedly well-defined translationally invariant average over $y \in R^\nu$.

Now our result is that there exists a solution of the foregoing axiom system such that

$$(\Omega, \varphi(Q(f_1), \cdots, Q(f_q))\Omega) = \mu_{f_1 \cdots f_q}(\varphi)$$

for all q, $f_1, \cdots, f_q, \varphi$. Conversely, every solution of the axiom system is realizable in this way (the "vacuum expectation values" in the formula determine the theory within unitary equivalence).

Let me say that to make the previous statement precise one uses, instead of the set E in R^ν, finite sets of points in large but bounded boxes contained in R^ν (large means that the limit of an infinite volume is taken). The measures $\mu_{f_1 \cdots f_q}$ arise in the description of correlations between positions of particles in classical equilibrium statistical mechanics (see Reference [2]).

From this result it can be seen with the naked eye that there are very many solutions to our axiom system because there are many different distribution patterns of points in R^ν.

References

1. Borchers, H. J., Nuovo Cimento, 24, 214 (1962).
2. Ruelle, D., J. Math. Phys., 6, 201 (1965).

3. Streater, R., and A. Wightman, PCT, Spin and Statistics and All That, W. A. Benjamin Inc., New York (1964).

4. Uhlmann, A., Wiss. Z., Karl-Marx-Univ., Leipzig, Math. Naturwiss. Reihe, 11, 213 (1962).

5. Wightman, A. S., in Proceedings of the Cargèse Summer School, 1964, ed. M. Lévy, Gordon & Breach, New York, 1966.

Chapter 8

QUANTIZATION AND DISPERSION FOR NONLINEAR RELATIVISTIC EQUATIONS

Irving Segal

1. Introduction

Our main purpose is to treat the dispersion (= scattering = collision) operator for a class of nonlinear relativistic partial differential equations, of which the equation

$$\Box\phi = m^2\phi + g\phi^3, \qquad m > 0,\ g > 0 \tag{1}$$

is typical. We wish to show in particular that for any sufficiently regular solution ϕ_0 of the "free" equation

$$\Box\phi_0 = m^2\phi_0, \tag{2}$$

there is a unique solution ϕ of the nonlinear Equation 1, to which ϕ_0 is suitably asymptotic as the time $t \to -\infty$; and that, following the propagation of the free solution ϕ_0 to the interacting field ϕ, ϕ in turn propagates as $t \to \infty$ to another solution ϕ_1 of the free equation $\Box\phi_1 = m^2\phi_1$; that is, ϕ is asymptotic to ϕ_1 as $t \to \infty$.

The general significance of this for relativistic physics is fairly clear; more specifically it indicates the following:

1. An important but generally rather unsatisfactory feature of the analysis of nonlinear systems in theoretical physics, namely the representation of the states of an interacting system in terms of the states of a physically somewhat idealistic free system, may be rigorously justifiable in realistic cases.
2. The interaction is automatically self-damping, so that no "adiabatic," unphysical, and mathematically uncontrolled "switching on and off" of the interaction is required, at least for a class of typical relevant systems.

The specific significance for quantum field theory is, however, much less clear. The classical equation is formally the same as the quantized one, but there is no prima facie connection between its solutions and that of the quantized equation. While the classical equation can readily be interpreted physically in a macroscopic situation, as, for example, in astrophysics, its microscopic significance is much less transparent. While applicable as an approximation at least to a beam of particles or states in which large numbers of particles are present, the classical equation lacks in itself a clear-cut connection with the problem of the propagation of states consisting of a small number of free particles, which is of course the physical problem with which quantum field theory is chiefly concerned.

Our explanation of the significance of the nonlinear classical equation for the corresponding quantized field may be organized around two main general theses:

1. In the case of a linear system, logically and physically it is essentially a group representation, rather than, in the first instance, a linear partial differential equation, which is the proper object of quantization.

2. Assuming our first thesis, the natural object to quantize in the nonlinear theory is a transformation group acting on a (nonlinear) manifold, rather than a nonlinear partial differential equation; the solution manifold of a nonlinear relativistic partial differential equation should provide an important example, and in particular be transformed appropriately by the Poincaré group.

The dispersion theory of the underlying classical differential equation is relevant to the further development of the second thesis. We shall not elaborate it here, other than to note that the problem of constructing a canonical measure in a space of classical wave functions or paths is one that has arisen in several connections; the construction of the classical "wave operator," which carries ϕ_0 into ϕ, is one way to approach this problem and provides, indeed, relevant temporally invariant measures in the solution manifold of the nonlinear partial differential equation in question.

Of course, the quantization procedure for a nonlinear transformation group on a manifold should be naturally coherent with the quantization procedure for a linear group representation, and should in particular reduce to it when the manifold is linear and the group acts linearly. Both theses require elaboration if their technical content is to be appreciated; for brevity we shall merely refer to several of our publications that provide most of this elaboration [5-8; 11; 12].

We turn now to the mathematical theory of dispersion for classical partial differential equations.

2. Mathematical Theory of Dispersion

Abstract framework. It is helpful in treating dispersion to take the underlying equations of motion in an abstract evolutionary form; we may as well take them at the same time in the integrated form which is generally convenient. This formulation is treated in detail in [10], and we shall merely recall briefly some notation and preliminary results.

Let B be a Banach space; by a forward propagator on B we mean a function $W(s,t)$ of pairs of real numbers s and t, with $s \geq t \geq 0$, to the continuous linear operators on B, which is strongly continuous as a function of s and t and which satisfies the identity: $W(r,s)W(s,t) = W(r,t)$, for $r \geq s \geq t$. (The term $W(s,t)$ may be thought of as describing the "free" motion.) Let there be given a continuous function $K(u,t)$ from $B \times T$ (where $T = [0,\infty)$) to B, which is locally Lipschitzian as a function of u uniformly on any finite subinterval of T. The nonlinear differential equation with which we are concerned takes the form

$$u(t) = W(t,0)u_0 + \int_0^t W(t,s)K(u(s),s)\,ds. \tag{3}$$

Here, u_0 (the Cauchy data at time 0) is given, and the problem is that of determining the function $u(t)$ from T to B satisfying Equation 3. Under the indicated conditions, there exists in some neighborhood of $t = 0$ a unique continuous solution to Equation 3.

The problem of the construction of the forward wave operator is rather analogous, except that the time $t = 0$ is replaced by the time $t = -\infty$, and that the datum at time $t = -\infty$ is itself time-dependent in a certain sense. In practice it is virtually always true that $W(t,s)$ has the form $V(t-s)$, but it is just as easy to treat the more general case.

Theorem 1. Let N be a homogeneous convex functional on the Banach space B with values in the interval $[0,\infty]$ such that if $u_n \to u$ in B, then $N(u) \leq \lim\sup_n N(u_n)$. Let t_0 be a given real number; let $W(t,s)$ be defined for all pairs of real numbers s and t such that $s \leq t \leq t_0$, as a continuous linear operator on B, and the propagator identity holds: $W(t,s)W(s,r) = W(t,r)$ if $r \leq s \leq t$; $W(s,s) = I$. Let $K(u,t)$ be a function with values in B defined when $N(u) < \infty$ and $t < t_0$, such that $K(0,t) = 0$.[1] Let $u_0(s)$ be a given bounded continuous function defined on the interval $(-\infty, t_0)$

[1] This condition is easily replaced by a convergence condition on $K(0,t)$.

such that $W(t, s)u_0(s) = u_0(t)$ if $s \leq t$. Then there exists a continuous function $u(t)$ from some interval $(-\infty, t_1)$ to the space $\underline{B}$ such that for $t < t_1$,

$$u(t) = u_0(t) + \int_{-\infty}^{t} W(t, s)K(u(s), s)\, ds, \tag{4}$$

the integral being absolutely convergent as a Riemann-Banach integral, provided the following conditions hold.

There must exist nonnegative real functions $g(p, q)$ and $h(p, q)$ on the quadrant $[0, \infty) \times [0, \infty)$, each of which is monotone increasing as a function of either p or q when the other variable is fixed; a monotone increasing real function $f(s)$ defined for $s < t_0$; and a positive number ε, such that:

For arbitrary u and v in $\underline{B}$, and with $p = \max[N(u), N(v)]$ and $q = \max(\|u\|, \|v\|)$, the following relations hold:

i. $N[W(t, s)K(u, s)] \leq g(p, q)$, where for any fixed value of r, $[f(t)]^{-1} \int_{-\infty}^{t} g[(1 + \varepsilon)f(s), r]\, ds \to 0$ as $t \to -\infty$.

ii. $\|W(t, s)[K(u, s) - K(v, s)]\| \leq h(p, q)\|u - v\|$, where for any fixed value of r, $\int_{-\infty} h[(1 + \varepsilon)f(s), r]\, ds < \infty$.

iii. $N[u_0(s)] \leq f(s)$.

iv. $W(t, s)K(u, s)$ is a continuous function of t, s, and u, in the topology of $\underline{B}$, for $s < t < t_0$ and u in any subset of $\underline{B}$ on which N is bounded.

Moreover, $N(u(t)) \leq (1 + \varepsilon)f(t)$ for $t < t_1$, and $u(t)$ is the unique solution of Equation 4 which is bounded (in $\underline{B}$) and satisfies this inequality.

Proof: Let c be a bound for $\|u_0(s)\|$ for $s < t_0$. Let t_1 be chosen so small that

$$[f(t)]^{-1} \int_{-\infty}^{t} g[(1 + \varepsilon)f(s),\ c + 1]\, ds < \varepsilon \text{ for } t < t_1,$$

$$(c + 1) \int_{-\infty}^{t_1} h[(1 + \varepsilon)f(s),\ c + 1]\, ds < 1.$$

As the basis for an induction argument, suppose that the functions $u_0(t), u_1(t), \cdots, u_n(t)$ exist and are continuous from the interval $(-\infty, t\,]$ into $\underline{B}$, and satisfy the following conditions for $k = 1, 2, \cdots, n$, with u_{-1} defined as 0:

$$u_k(t) = u_0(t) + \int_{-\infty}^{t} W(t, s)K(u_{k-1}(s), s)\, ds, \qquad (5)$$

absolutely convergent integral,

and

$$N(u_k(t)) \le (1 + \varepsilon)f(t), \qquad \|u_k(t)\| \le c + 1. \qquad (6)$$

We note that these relations are in any event valid when $n = 0$.

Now consider the integral $\int_{-\infty}^{t} W(t, s)K[u_n(s), s]\, ds$, where $t < t_1$. The integrand is a continuous function of s with values in $\underline{B}$, by the induction hypothesis and condition iv. Moreover, it satisfies by condition ii the inequality

$$\|W(t, s)K[u_n(s), s]\| \le h((1 + \varepsilon)f(s), c + 1)(c + 1).$$

The integral is therefore absolutely convergent, and a function $u_{n+1}(t)$ is well defined by Equation 5, with k replaced by $n + 1$. By virtue of condition iv, the integrand is a continuous function of t. As we have just seen it is dominated by an integrable function of s, independently of the value of t; it follows that $u_{n+1}(t)$ is a continuous function of t.

To complete the inductive definition of the sequence $\{u_m(t);\ m = 0, 1, 2, \cdots\}$, let us check the validity of the inequalities 6 with k replaced by $n + 1$. To this end, observe first that if $\int F(t)\, dt$ is any absolutely convergent Riemann integral of a function with values in $\underline{B}$ such that $N(F(t)) \le \phi(t)$, where $\phi(t)$ is a continuous function, then $N(\int F(t)\, dt) \le \int \phi(t)\, dt$. For, employing approximating Riemann sums,

$$N\left(\int F(t)\, dt\right) = N(\lim \Sigma_i F(t_i)m_i) \le \limsup N(\Sigma_i F(t_i)m_i)$$

$$\le \limsup \Sigma_i N(F(t_i))m_i \le \limsup \Sigma_i \phi(t_i)m_i$$

$$\to \int \phi(t)\, dt.$$

In particular,

$$N(u_{n+1}(t)) \le f(t) + \int_{-\infty}^{t} N(W(t, s)K(u_n(s), s))\, ds$$

$$\le f(t) + \int_{-\infty}^{t} g((1 + \varepsilon)f(s), c + 1)\, ds,$$

which, by the manner in which t_1 was chosen, is bounded in turn for $t < t_1$ by

$$f(t) + \varepsilon f(t) = (1 + \varepsilon)f(t).$$

On the other hand, for $t < t_1$,

$$\|u_{n+1}(t)\| \leq \int_{-\infty}^{t} h((1 + \varepsilon)f(s), c + 1)(c + 1)\, ds < \|u_{n+1}(t)\|$$

$$\leq \|u_0(t)\| + \int_{-\infty}^{t} h((1 + \varepsilon)f(s), c + 1)(c + 1)\, ds < c + 1$$

by conditions iii and the manner of choice of t_1. The induction is therefore complete.

Now taking the difference of successive equations 5, and making use of the inequalities 6 and the conditions i and ii of Theorem 1, for $n = 0, 1, 2 \cdots$, we obtain

$$\|u_{n+1}(t) - u_n(t)\| \leq \int_{-\infty}^{t} h((1 + \varepsilon)f(s), c + 1)\|u_n(s) - u_{n-1}(s)\|\, ds.$$

The integrability of $h((1 + \varepsilon)f(s), c + 1)$ as a function of s now implies in a well-known fashion the uniform convergence of the sequence $u_m(t)$ in $\underline{B}$ to a continuous function $u(t)$ from the interval $(-\infty, t_0)$ into $\underline{B}$. Since $N(u(t)) \leq \limsup_m N[u_m(t)]$, it follows that $N[u(t)] \leq (1 + \varepsilon)f(t)$. To show that $u(t)$ satisfies Equation 4, note that $\int_{-\infty}^{t_1} W(t, s)K(u(s), s)\, ds$ is absolutely convergent by ii and the estimate on $N(u(t))$ just obtained. Writing

$$u(t) - u_0(t) - \int_{-\infty}^{t} W(t, s)K(u(s), s)\, ds$$

$$= \lim_m \int_{-\infty}^{t} W(t, s)[K(u_m(s), s) - K(u(s), s)]\, ds,$$

the norm in $\underline{B}$ of the left-hand side of the foregoing equation is bounded by

$$\limsup_m \int_{-\infty}^{t} \|W(t, s)[K(u_m(s), s) - K(u(s), s)]\|\, ds$$

which in turn is bounded by

$$\lim\sup_m \int_{-\infty}^{t} h[(1+\varepsilon)f(s), c+1]\|u_m(s) - u(s)\|\, ds.$$

This expression converges to zero by the integrability of $h[(1+\varepsilon)f(s), c+1]$ and the uniform convergence to zero of $\|u_m(s) - u(s)\|$. The uniqueness of u(t) as a solution in the indicated class follows in a similar fashion. End of proof.

The wave operator for scalar equations. Theorem 1 implies that the wave operator exists for any nonlinear relativistic quasilinear partial differential equation of the usual type, provided the nonlinear term is of sufficiently high degree and the incoming field (i.e. the datum at time $-\infty$) is sufficiently regular. On the other hand, the higher this degree, the more difficult it is, in general, to establish uniqueness, regularity, and global existence. Thus there is a conflict between the types of assumptions, regarding the interaction, which lead to strong results on existence and other commonly studied features of solutions of differential equations, and assumptions which lead to strong results in dispersion theory. There is nevertheless a significant class of equations for which all of these features are in evidence.

These matters are easily illustrated through the consideration of scalar relativistic equations of the type

$$\Box\phi = m^2\phi + g\phi^p, \tag{7}$$

where $\Box = \Delta - \partial^2/\partial t^2$, Δ designating the Laplacian on the space whose dimension will be denoted n. If $n \leq 3$, $p = 3$, and $g \geq 0$, then Equation 7 has a unique global solution for arbitrarily prescribed Cauchy data of finite energy at any time. If however, $g < 0$, this is not the case, and it is not known whether there exist any global finite energy solutions other than 0. Nevertheless, in either case there will exist for any given sufficiently regular solution ϕ_0 of the "free" equation

$$\Box\phi_0 = m^2\phi_0, \tag{8}$$

a solution ϕ of Equation 7 valid throughout space, and for all times t in some infinite interval $(-\infty, t_0)$, which is asymptotic to ϕ_0 as $t \to -\infty$. The same is indeed true for arbitrary values of $p \geq 3$, although the global existence of solutions is known only when p is odd and $g \geq 0$, and is unlikely to be valid for even values of p or when $g < 0$.

Some implications of Theorem 1 for the existence of the forward wave operator for scalar relativistic equations are given in the following theorem.

Theorem 2. Let ϕ_0 be a finite-energy solution of the equation

$$\Box\phi_0 = m^2\phi_0, \quad m > 0.$$

Let F be a given continuously differentiable function of a real variable. Then there exists a finite-energy solution ϕ of the (integral form of) equation

$$\Box\phi = m^2\phi + F(\phi)$$

in an interval of the form $-\infty < t < t_0$, which is strongly asymptotic (in the energy norm) to ϕ_0 as $t \to -\infty$, provided (a) the number of space dimensions is 1, 2, or 3; (b) $F(\lambda) = 0(|\lambda|^{a+1})$ and $F'(\lambda) = 0(|\lambda|^a)$ near $\lambda = 0$, for some $a > 0$; (c) there exists a monotone increasing function f(t) such that $|\phi_0(\vec{x}, t)| \leq f(t)$ and such that $(f(t))^{-1} \int_{-\infty}^{t} f(s)^a \to 0$ for $t \to -\infty$.

Furthermore, the solution ϕ satisfies the inequality

$$|\phi(\vec{x}, t)| \leq (1 + \varepsilon)f(t)$$

for any $\varepsilon > 0$, if t_0 is appropriately chosen, and is unique within this class of solutions.

Proof:[2] Let S denote the physical (Euclidean) space in question, and $L_2(S)$ the space of all real-valued square-integrable functions on S, relative to the inner product $\langle x, y\rangle = \int x(p)\,\overline{y}(p)\,d$ where dp denotes the element of Lebesgue measure in the Euclidea space S. Let B denote the positive self-adjoint operator $(m^2 I - \Delta)$ in $L_2(S)$, and let $[\underline{D}_B]$ denote the domain of B as a Hilbert space relative to the inner product $\langle x, y\rangle' = \langle Bx, By\rangle$. Let $\underline{H}$ denote the Hilbert space direct sum of $[\underline{D}_B]$ with $L_2(S)$. Let $[x, y]$ denote the element of $\underline{H}$ with component x in $[\underline{D}_B]$ and component y in $L_2(S)$. Let $W_0(t)$ denote the one-parameter continuous group of orthogonal transformations on $\underline{H}$ whose matrix, relative to the decomposition defining $\underline{H}$, has the form:

$$W_0(t) = \begin{bmatrix} \cos(tB) & -\dfrac{\sin(tB)}{B} \\ B\sin(tB) & \cos(tB) \end{bmatrix}.$$

[2]The method of proof is applicable to relativistic equations of higher spin in the indicated number of space dimensions.

We define $K([x, y], s) = [0, F(x)]$. Let the convex nonnegative functional N be defined on $\underline{H}$ by the equation $N([x, y]) = \|x\|_\infty$ (where for any measurable function u on S, $\|u\|_p$ denotes the norm in $L_p(S)$; in particular, $\|u\|_\infty$ equals the essential supremum of u). Let $u_0(t) = [\phi_0(t), \dot{\phi}_0(t)]$, where for any function $\psi(\vec{x}, t)$ on space time (with $\vec{x} \in S$ and t real), we denote by $\psi(t)$ the mapping from the reals to the space of measurable functions on S defined by ψ; that is, $\psi(t) = \psi(\bullet, t)$ in the notation of Moore. Our assertion is then that Equation 4, of Theorem 1 with $W(t, s) = W_0(t - s)$ has a solution with the indicated properties.

We check successively the hypotheses of Theorem 1. The limiting condition on the auxiliary norm N is an immediate consequence of the fact that convergence of a sequence $L_2(S)$ implies convergence of a subsequence almost everywhere. There is no difficulty in checking the required properties of $W(t, s)$. The condition that $W(t, s)u_0(s) = u_0(t)$ means only that $u_0(s)$ is a solution of the "free" equation, which is immediately implied by the corresponding given equation for ϕ_0. The boundedness and the continuity of $u_0(t)$ are implied by the orthogonality and the strong continuity as a function of t of $W_0(t)$.

To verify i of Theorem 1 note that

$$N(W(t, s)K(u, s)) = \left\| \frac{\sin (tB)}{B} F(x) \right\|_\infty = \left\| \frac{\sin (tB)}{B^2} BF(x) \right\|_\infty$$

provided F(x) is in $\underline{D_B}$. By the theorem of Plancherel, the operator $\sin (tB)/B^2$ is transformed by the Fourier transformation into that of multiplication by the function $\sin [t(m^2 + R^2)^{(1/2)}]/(m^2 + R^2)$, where R denotes the distance from the origin in the space dual to S. This function is evidently square-integrable, and is in fact of uniformly bounded L_2-norm, in case $n = 1, 2$, or 3. It follows that $\sin (tB)/B^2$ may be represented as the operator of convolution with a kernel L_t such that $\|L_t\|_2$ is bounded as a function of t. It results from Schwarz's inequality that

$$N(W(t, s)K(u, s)) \leq \text{const} \|BF(x)\|_2,$$

provided $F(x) \in \underline{D_B}$.

The following result will now prove useful.

> Lemma 1. If k is an arbitrary function in $L_2(R^p) \cap L_\infty(R^p)$ that is in the domain of the partial differentiation operator $\partial/\partial x_j$ in its usual formulation as a normal operator in $L_2(R^p)$, a generic point in R^p being represented as $(x_1, x_2, \cdots, x_p)$, then for any C^1 function F of a real variable, F(k(x)) is in the domain of $\partial/\partial x_j$ in $L_2(R^p)$, and $(\partial/\partial x_j)F(k(x)) = F'(k(x))(\partial k/\partial x_j)$.

Proof: The conclusion is clear if k is sufficiently smooth, for example, if k is equivalent to a C^1 function on R^p. To treat the case of an arbitrary function k of the indicated type, choose a sequence k_n such that (a) $k_n \to k$ in $L_2(R^n)$ and almost everywhere, (b) $\|k_n\|_\infty$ is bounded as a function of n, (c) $(\partial/\partial x_j)k_n \to (\partial/\partial x_j)k$ in $L_2(R^n)$. Specifically, k_n may be chosen to have the form $k_n = k * d_n$, where d_n is a sequence of nonnegative C^∞ functions of integral unity on R^p and support contained in the sphere of radius n^{-1} around the origin. Then for each n,

$$\left(\frac{\partial}{\partial x_j}\right)F(k_n(x)) = F'(k_n(x))\left(\frac{\partial}{\partial x_j}\right)k_n(x);$$

$F'(k_n(x)) \to F'(k(x))$ almost everywhere and boundedly; consequently the right-hand side of the foregoing equation converges in $L_2(R^n)$ to $F'(k(x))(\partial/\partial x_j)k(x)$. On the other hand, $F(k_n(x)) - F(k(x)) = F'(\lambda)(k_n(x) - k(x))$, where λ remains bounded as a function of x and n, so that $F(k_n(x)) \to F(k(x))$ in $L_2(R^n)$. The conclusion of the lemma now follows from the fact that $\partial/\partial x_j$ is a closed operator.

Now if z is in the domain of B^2 in $L_2(S)$,

$$\|Bz\|_2^2 = \langle Bz, Bz\rangle = \langle B^2 z, z\rangle = \langle (m^2 I - \Delta)z, z\rangle$$

$$= m^2\|z\|_2^2 + \|\text{grad } z\|_2^2.$$

If z is only in the domain of B, it may be approximated by elements of the domain of B^2 in the space $[\underline{D}_B]$, with the result that

$$\|Bz\|_2^2 = m^2\|z\|_2^2 + \|\text{grad } z\|_2^2.$$

In particular, with use of Lemma 1, it follows that

$$\|BF(x)\|_2^2 = m^2\|F(x)\|_2^2 + \|F'(x) \text{ grad } x\|_2^2.$$

Now $\|F(x)\|_2 = \|F_0(x)x\|_2$, where $F_0(\lambda) = F(\lambda)/\lambda$, so that

$$\|F(x)\|_2 \leq \|F_0(x)\|_\infty\|x\|_2 \leq G_0(\|x\|_\infty)\|x\|_2,$$

where $G_0(\lambda) = \sup_{|\lambda'|\leq\lambda} |F_0(\lambda')|$. Similarly,

$$\|F'(x) \text{ grad } x\|_2 \leq \|F'(x)\|_\infty\|\text{grad } x\|_2 \leq G_1(\|x\|_\infty)\|\text{grad } x\|_2,$$

where $G_1(\lambda) = \sup_{|\lambda'|\leq|\lambda|} |F'(\lambda')|$.

The foregoing may be summarized in the inequality

$$\|BF(x)\|_2 \leq \|u\| G_{01}(N(u)),$$

where $G_{01}(\lambda) = \max[G_0(\lambda), G_1(\lambda)]$. Now set $g(p, q) = \text{const}\ G_{01}(p)q$; condition i of Theorem 1 follows, by virtue of the condition on f(s) in the hypotheses of Theorem 2.

To verify condition ii of Theorem 1 note that

$$\|F(x) - F(y)\|_2 = \|\{[F(x) - F(y)]/(x - y)\}(x - y)\|_2$$

$$\leq \|(F(x) - F(y))/(x - y)\|_\infty \|x - y\|_2;$$

By the mean-value theorem,

$$\left\|\frac{F(x) - F(y)}{x - y}\right\|_\infty \leq G_1(\max(\|x\|_\infty, \|y\|_\infty));$$

by virtue of the boundedness of B^{-1}, $\|x - y\|_2 \leq \text{const}\ \|B(x - y)\|_2$. It follows that condition ii holds with h(p, q) defined as const $G_1(p)$; the integrability condition in ii is an immediate consequence of the given condition on f(s).

Condition iii is a matter of assumption. Finally, condition iv is implied by the continuity of K(u, s), by virtue of the strong continuity of W(s, t) as a function of s and t. This continuity of K(u, s) means that $F(x) \to F(y)$ in case $x \to y$ in $[\underline{D}_B]$, with $\|x\|_\infty$ remaining bounded. This is an immediate consequence of the bound obtained in the preceding paragraph. End of proof.

The wave operator in higher dimensions. In order to treat the case of a higher-dimensional space S, it is necessary to modify the space $\underline{H}$ and the norm N. The general way to do this suitably can be developed within the framework of Theorem 1 from the specific treatment for the cases n = 4 or 5 given in the following theorem:

Theorem 3. Let ϕ_0 be a given finite-energy solution of the (integral form of the) equation $\Box\phi_0 = m^2\phi_0 (m > 0)$, whose spatial derivatives of third order and less also have finite energy; let F be a given function of class C^3; let the number of space dimensions be 4 or 5. Then there exists a finite-energy solution ϕ of the (integral form of the) equation $\Box\phi = m^2\phi + F(\phi)$ in an interval of the form $-\infty < t < t_0$, which is strongly asymptotic (in the energy and uniform norms) to ϕ_0 as $t \to -\infty$, provided: (a) $F^j(\lambda) = 0(|\lambda|^{a+1-j})$ near $\lambda = 0$ for j = 0, 1, 2, 3 and some a > 0; (b) there exists a monotone increasing function f(t) such that $|\phi_0(\vec{x}, t)|$

and $|\text{grad } \phi_0(\vec{x}, t)|$ are bounded by f(t), and

$$(f(t))^{-1} \int_{-\infty}^{t} f(s)^{a}\, ds \to 0 \text{ as } t \to -\infty, \quad \int_{-\infty}^{t} f(t)^{a-1}\, dt < \infty.$$

Proof: Let $\underline{H}_b$ denote the Hilbert space direct sum of $[\underline{D}_{B^{b+1}}] + [\underline{D}_{B^b}]$, where b is a given positive number, and we use the notation $[\underline{D}_T]$ for the Hilbert space that consists of the domain of the self-adjoint operator T, assumed invertible, relative to the inner product $\langle x, y\rangle_T = \langle Tx, Ty\rangle$. The space $\underline{H}_0$ is then identical with the space $\underline{H}$ used in the proof of Theorem 2. Now for the present case we use as the Banach space $\underline{B}$ of Theorem 1 the subset $\underline{H}_2^\infty$ of $\underline{H}_2$ consisting of elements $[x, y]$ for which $\|x\|_\infty < \infty$; the norm $\|u\|$ in $\underline{B}$ is defined as $\|u\|_2 + \|u\|_\infty$, where $\|u\|_2^2 = \|B^3x\|_2^2 + \|B^2y\|_2^2$, and $\|u\|_\infty = \|x\|_\infty$. The propagator W(s, t) is defined by the same matrix; it remains an orthogonal transformation on $\underline{H}_2$ which depends in a continuous fashion (in the strong operator topology) on s and t. For any vector $u = [x, y]$ in $\underline{B}$, let N(u) be defined as $\|x\|_\infty + \|\text{grad } x\|_\infty$ (where $\|\text{grad } x\|_\infty = \Sigma_i \|x_i\|$ here x_i denotes the partial derivative of x with respect to the ith spatial coordinate).

Now consider the verification of the hypotheses of Theorem 1. $u_n \to u$ in $\underline{B}$ (where $u_n = [x_n, w_n]$), then in particular $\|B^3(x_n - x)\|_2$ by virtue of the boundedness of B^{-1}, it follows that $\|B(x_n - x)\|_2 \to$ This implies (see, for example, the proof of Theorem 2) that $\|\text{grad } (x_n - x)\|_2 \to 0$; it then follows, as in the proof of Theorem that $\|\text{grad } x\|_\infty \leq \lim \sup_n \|\text{grad } x_n\|_\infty$. Deferring the considera tion of W(s, t) so that it may be combined with the examination of $u_0(s)$, let us consider the properties of K(u, s), which is defined in the same fashion as in Theorem 2: $K([x, y], s) = [0, F(x)]$. If $x \in \underline{D}_{B^3}$ and $N(u) < \infty$, then by Lemma 1,

$$B^2F(x) = m^2F(x) - F''(x)\Sigma_i x_i^2 - F'(x)\Delta x.$$

Now with $G_0(\lambda) = \sup_{|\lambda'|<\lambda} |F(\lambda')\lambda'^{-1}|$ and $G_i(\lambda) = \sup_{|\lambda'|<\lambda} |F^{(i)}($ $(i = 1, 2, \cdots)$, we have the following estimates:

$$\|B^2F(x)\|_2 \leq m^2G_0(\|x\|_\infty)\|x\|_2 + G_1(\|x\|_\infty)\|\Delta x\|_2$$

$$+ G_2(\|x\|_\infty)\|\text{grad } x\|_\infty\|\text{grad } x\|_2.$$

In particular, for $u \in \underline{B}$ such that $N(u) < \infty$, K(u, t) is a well-defined element of $\underline{B}$. Since K(u, s) is independent of the variable s, the continuity of the mapping $(u, s) \to K(u, s)$ relative to any set on which $N(u)$ is bounded is a consequence of condition ii of Theorem 1, to be verified later.

Now let $u_0(s)$ be defined (as before) as $[\Phi_0(s), \mathring{\Phi}_0(s)]$. To treat its continuity and boundedness, we utilize a more general lemma.

> Lemma 2. Let ϕ be a solution of the equation $\Box\phi = m^2\phi$ in n space dimensions which has all of its spatial derivatives of an order c, where $c > n/2 - 1$, of finite energy. Then the mapping $t \to \Phi(t)$ $(=\phi(\bullet, t))$ is uniformly continuous and bounded from R^1 into $L_\infty(S)$.

Proof: The energy of the solution ϕ may be expressed as $\|B\Phi(t)\|_2^2 + \|\dot{\Phi}(t)\|_2^2$, for any time t. That ϕ has spatial derivatives of order c which are of finite energy means that $\Phi(t)$ is in the domain of B^{1+c} and that $\dot{\Phi}(t)$ is in the domain of B^c (for some particular time t, or equivalently, in view of the conservation of energy, for all times). Hence

$$\Phi(t) = \cos(tB)\Phi(0) + \frac{\sin(tB)}{B}\dot{\Phi}(0)$$

$$= \frac{\cos(tB)}{B^{1+c}}(B^{1+c}\Phi(0)) + \frac{\sin(tB)}{B^c}(B^c\dot{\Phi}(0)).$$

Now for any $c > n/2 - 1$, e^{itB}/B^{1+c} is the operation of convolution by a kernel in L_2, which depends uniformly continuously on t in the L_2-norm by an application of the Plancherel theorem similar to that made in the proof of Theorem 1, and is uniformly bounded in $L_2(S)$. Thus

$$\Phi(t) = L_t * x + M_t * y,$$

where x and y are fixed elements of $L_2(S)$, while $t \to L_t$ and $t \to M_t$ are continuous maps of R^1 into $L_2(S)$. Applying Schwarz's inequality, it follows that

$$\|\Phi(t)\|_\infty \leq \|L_t\|_2\|x\|_2 + \|M_t\|_2\|y\|_2 \leq \text{const},$$

and that

$$\|\Phi(t) - \Phi(t')\|_\infty \leq \|L_t - L_{t'}\|_2\|x\|_2 + \|M_t - M_{t'}\|_2\|y\|_2 \to 0$$

as $t - t' \to 0$.

In the present case, $n \leq 5$, so that any $c > 1.5$ may be used. Now if ϕ has c space derivatives of finite energy, grad ϕ will have components that are solutions of the same equation having c - 1 space derivatives of finite energy. In particular, for the given ϕ_0 for which $B^3\phi_0$ is again of finite energy (note that it is also a solution of the indicated equation), grad ϕ_0 will have components that have space derivatives of second order of finite energy. It follows that $u_0(t)$ is a bounded and continuous function of t, in the N-norm, and that W(t, s) is continuous in the $\|x\|_\infty$ pseudonorm. It follows as before, that $W(t, s)u_0(s) = u_0(s)$, and by virtue of the continuity and orthogonality of the action of W(s, t) on $\underline{H}_b$ for all b, the boundedness and continuity of $u_0(t)$ in the $\underline{H}_b$-norm also holds. The continuity of W(t, s) in the $\|x\|_\infty$-pseudonorm and its orthogonality on $\underline{H}_b$ together imply its continuity as an operator on $\underline{B}$.

To treat condition i, let ε be an arbitrary positive number, take f(t) as in Theorem 3, and set $u = [x, w]$. The first component of W(t, s)K(u, s) is $[\sin((t - s)B)/B]F(x)$; thus, with $r = t - s$,

$$N[W(t, s)K(u, s)] = \left\|\frac{\sin(rB)}{B} F(x)\right\|_\infty + \left\|\frac{\sin(rB)}{B} \text{grad } F(x)\right\|_\infty .$$

Now

$$\left\|\frac{\sin(rB)}{B} F(x)\right\|_\infty = \left\|\frac{\sin(rB)}{B^3}[B^2F(x)]\right\|_\infty \leq \text{const } \|B^2F(x)\|_2,$$

by the same argument as in the proof of Theorem 2. Now computing, with the aid of Lemma 1,

$$B^2F(x) = m^2F(x) - F'(x)\Delta x - F''(x)\Sigma_i x_i^2 .$$

The first term on the right-hand side may be estimated as follows: $\|F(x)\|_2 \leq \|F(x)/x\|_\infty \|x\|_2$. By virtue of the boundedness of B^{-1},

$$\|F(x)\|_2 \leq \text{const } G_0(\|x\|_\infty)\|B^3x\|_2 \leq \text{const } G_0(N(u))\|u\| .$$

To estimate the second term in $B^2F(x)$, note that

$$\|F'(x)\Delta x\|_2 \leq \|F'(x)\|_\infty \|\Delta x\|_2 \leq G_1(\|x\|_\infty) \text{ const } \|B^3x\|_2$$

$$\leq \text{const } G_1(N(u))\|u\| .$$

The third term is

$$\|F''(x)\Sigma_i x_i^2\|_2 \leq \|F''(x)\|_\infty \|\text{grad } x\|_\infty \|\text{grad } x\|_2$$

$$\leq G_2(\|x\|_\infty)\|\text{grad } x\|_\infty \text{ const } \|B^3 x\|_2$$

$$\leq \text{const } G_2[N(u)]N(u)\|u\|.$$

Now consider $\|[\sin(rB)/B] \text{ grad } F(x)\|_\infty$; this is similarly bounded by const $\Sigma_i \|B^2 \partial_i F(x)\|_2$. A computation employing Lemma 1 shows that

$$\partial_j^2 \partial_i F(x) = F'''(x)(\partial_j x)^2 \partial_i x + F''(x)(\partial_j^2 x)(\partial_i x) + 2F''(x)(\partial_j x)(\partial_j \partial_i x)$$

$$+ F'(x)(\partial_j^2 \partial_i x).$$

Recalling that $B^2 = m^2 I - \Delta$ and that $\|\partial_j \partial_i x\|_2^2 \leq \|\partial_j^2 x\|_2 \|\partial_i^2 x\|_2$, it results that

$$\|B^2 \partial_i F(x)\|_2 \leq G_3(\|x\|_\infty)\|\text{grad } x\|_\infty^2 \|\text{grad } x\|_2$$

$$+ G_2(\|x\|_\infty)\|\text{grad } x\|_\infty \|\Delta x\|_2$$

$$+ 2G_2(\|x\|_\infty)\|\text{grad } x\|_\infty \|\Delta x\|_2 + G_1(\|x\|_\infty)\|B^3 x\|_2.$$

Hence

$$\|B^2 \text{ grad } F(x)\|_2 \leq \text{const } G_{0123}(N(u))\|u\|,$$

where $G_{0123}(\lambda)$ is a monotone increasing function of λ which is $O(\lambda^a)$ for $\lambda \to 0$. Condition i now follows with f(t) as given earlier.

Now consider condition ii of Theorem 1. Then

$$\|W(t, s)[K(u, s) - K(v, s)]\| = \|W(t, s)[K(u, s) - K(v, s)]\|_{\underline{H}_b}$$

$$+ \left\| \frac{\sin((t - s)B)}{B} (F(x) - F(y)) \right\|_\infty.$$

Since W(t, s) is an orthogonal transformation on $\underline{H}_b$, the first term on the right-hand side of the preceding equation is bounded by

$$\|K(u, s) - K(v, s)\|_{\underline{H}_b} = \|B^2(F(x) - F(y))\|_2$$

$$\leq m^2 \|F(x) - F(y)\|_2 + \|\Delta F(x) - \Delta F(y)\|_2.$$

To bound the first term on the right-hand side of the preceding equation, note that

$$\|F(x) - F(y)\|_2 \leq \|x - y\|_2 \left\| \frac{F(x) - F(y)}{x - y} \right\|_\infty,$$

which by the mean-value theorem is bounded by $\|x - y\|_2 G_1(\max(\|x\|_\infty, \|y\|_\infty))$. With regard to the second term, note that $\Delta F(x) = F''(x)(\text{grad } x)^2 + F'(x)\Delta x$; then

$$\Delta F(x) - \Delta F(y) = [F''(x)(\text{grad } x)^2 - F''(y)(\text{grad } y)^2]$$

$$+ (F'(x)\Delta x - F'(y)\Delta y).$$

The first term in the foregoing expression for $\Delta F(x) - \Delta F(y)$ may be expressed as $(F''(x) - F''(y))(\text{grad } x)^2 + F''(y)[(\text{grad } x)^2 - (\text{grad } y$ whose norm in $L_2(S)$ is bounded by $\|F''(x) - F''(y)\|_2 \|\text{grad } x\|_\infty^2 + \|F''(y)\|_\infty \|(\text{grad } x)^2 - (\text{grad } y)^2\|_2$. By arguments similar to those employed earlier in this proof, this in turn is bounded by $G_3(\|x\|_\infty)\|x - y\|_2 \|\text{grad } x\|_\infty^2 + G_2(\|y\|_\infty)\|\text{grad } x - \text{grad } y\|_2(\|\text{grad } x\|$ $\|\text{grad } y\|_\infty)$. By way of summary, the first term in the expressio above for $\Delta F(x) - \Delta F(y)$ is bounded by const $G_3(N(u))N(u)^2\|u - v\|$ $G_2(N(v))(N(u) + N(v))\|u - v\|$.

The remaining term in the expression for $\Delta F(x) - \Delta F(y)$ may be expressed as $F'(x)(\Delta x - \Delta y) + [F'(x) - F'(y)]\Delta y$, which is dominate in norm $\|\bullet\|$ by

$$\text{const } G_1(\|x\|_\infty)\|\Delta x - \Delta y\| + G_2(\max(\|x\|_\infty, \|y\|_\infty))\|x - y\|_\infty \|\Delta y\|$$

$$\leq \text{const } G_1(N(u))\|u - v\| + \text{const } G_2(\max[N(u), N(v)])\|v\| N(u -$$

Adding terms gives the result

$$\|W(t, s)[K(u, s) - K(v, s)]\|$$

$$\leq \text{const } [G_1(N(u)) + G_2(N(v)) \max(N(u), N(v))$$

$$+ G_3(N(u))N(u)^2] \|u - v\| + \text{const } G_2(\max[N(u), N(v)])\|v\| N(u$$

$$\leq h_1(p, q)\|u - v\|,$$

with p and q as in Theorem 2, where for any fixed r, $h_1(\lambda, r) = O(|\lambda|)^a$.

To complete the consideration of condition ii, it remains to examine $\|[\sin(rB)/B](F(x) - F(y))\|_\infty$. As before, this can be supplanted by the consideration of $\|B^2(F(x) - F(y))\|_2$; this is the same as the term which has just been considered at length. It follows that if $h(p, q)$ is defined as const $\times\, h_1(p, q)$, then ii is satisfied. In view of the independence of $K(u, s)$ from s, it follows also that condition iv is satisfied. Condition iii is satisfied by hypothesis (the $f(s)$ of Theorem 1 being defined as twice the $f(s)$ of Theorem 3 leaves the remainder of the argument totally unaffected). The conclusion of Theorem 3 has now been subsumed under that of Theorem 1. End of proof.

The treatment of the case of an arbitrary number of space dimensions can be given along entirely similar lines; a detailed proof will be given elsewhere. It may be noted that quasi-relativistic nonlinear equations, of the form

$$\Box\phi = m^2\phi + F(\phi, \operatorname{grad}\phi, \dot{\phi}),$$

may be treated in a quite analogous fashion. A general result including this case could be given, but it would either be quite complicated or lack the specificity required for applications in the present direction. We therefore turn now to the consideration of the qualitatively different questions which are involved in these applications.

Asymptotic decay of solutions of linear relativistic equations. In order to verify the hypotheses of Theorems 2 and 3 for a suitably dense subset of free solutions ϕ_0, it is necessary to have information on the decay of these solutions in the L_∞-norm as $|t| \to \infty$; one might consider also the question of the decay in the L_p-norm for $p > 2$, but no results in this direction are at present known which are stronger than those deducible from the consideration of the L_∞-norm. This question of linear decay was treated in detail in work by A. R. Brodsky [3] under our direction, and we shall follow the method developed there. It is sufficient for our present purposes to show the following lemma.

Lemma 3. For any solution ψ of finite energy of the (integral form of the) equation $\Box\psi = m^2\psi$ $(m > 0)$ in n space dimensions, one has the inequality

$$\|\psi(t)\|_\infty \leq C(t)\,|||[\psi(0), \dot{\psi}(0)]|||,$$

where $C(t)$ is a continuous function of t which is $0(|t|^{-n/2})$ for $|t| \to \infty$ and $|||[x, y]|||$ is defined, relative to a given positive number ε, by the equation $|||[x, y]||| = \|e^{\varepsilon B} Bx\|_1 + \|e^{\varepsilon B} y\|_1$.[3]

Proof: We may write

$$\Phi(t) = \cos(tB)\,\Phi(0) + \frac{\sin(tB)}{B}\,\dot{\Phi}(0).$$

If the Fourier transforms of $\Phi(0)$ and $\dot{\Phi}(0)$ are, after multiplication by $\exp[\varepsilon(m^2 + R^2)^{1/2}](m^2 + R^2)^{1/2}$ and $\exp[\varepsilon(m^2 + R^2)^{1/2}]$, respectively, the Fourier transforms of functions in $L_1(S)$ (here R is the radius vector in the space dual to S), then as a matter of definition, $\Phi(0)$ and $\dot{\Phi}(0)$ are in the respective domains of $e^{\varepsilon B} B$ and B, and we may write

$$\Phi(t) = \left(e^{-\varepsilon B}\,\frac{\cos(tB)}{B}\right)[e^{\varepsilon B}\,B\Phi(0)] + \left(e^{-\varepsilon B}\,\frac{\sin(tB)}{B}\right)[e^{\varepsilon B}\,\dot{\Phi}(0)].$$

Now the operator $B^{-1} e^{-(\varepsilon + it)B}$ is that of convolution with a kernel $L_{t,\varepsilon}(\vec{x})$ which is square-integrable over S, by Plancherel's theorem and, by taking L_∞ norms in the foregoing equation, it results that

---

[3]The $t^{-n/2}$ decay rate is best possible for a power law. To see this, it suffices (see Brodsky [3]) to treat the case n = 1. Indeed, a stronger statement can be made.

If $\phi(x, t)$ is a normalizable solution of the equation $\Box\phi = m^2\phi$ in one space dimension such that $\phi(x, t)$ is square-integrable as a function of t for some fixed x, then the Fourier transform of ϕ can not be integrable, continuous, and nonvanishing on the mass hyperboloid.

For on setting

$$\phi(x, t) = \int \frac{\exp\{i[xy - t(m^2 + y^2)^{1/2}]\}}{(m^2 + y^2)^{1/2}}\, f(y)\, dy,$$

and letting $y = (u^2 - 1)^{1/2}$, where $|u| \geq 1$, the foregoing representation becomes

$$\phi(x, t) = \int_{|u| \geq 1} \frac{g(u)\, e^{-itu}}{(u^2 - 1)^{1/2}}\, f[y(u)]\, du,$$

where g(u) does not depend on t and is of absolute value 1. If $\phi(x, t)$ is square-integrable as a function of t, then by the Plancherel theorem, $f(y(u))(u^2 - 1)^{-1/2}$ must be square-integrable on the region $[u: |u| > 1]$. Since $(u^2 - 1)^{-1/2}$ is obviously not such, it follows that f(y(u)) must vanish for u = 1.

$$\|\Phi(t)\|_\infty \leq \|L_{t,\varepsilon}\|_\infty[\|e^{\varepsilon B}\, B\Phi(0)\|_1 + \|e^{\varepsilon B}\,\dot{\Phi}(0)\|_1]$$

(employing the general principle that $\|A * B\|_\infty \leq \|A\|_\infty \|B\|_1$). The kernel $L_{t,\varepsilon}(\vec{x})$ is however known explicitly.[4] It is the inverse Fourier transform of the radial function

$$\exp[-(\varepsilon + it)(m^2 + R^2)^{1/2}](m^2 + R^2)^{-1/2},$$

where R is the distance from the origin in the space dual to S. As is well known, such a transform may be reduced to a one-dimensional transform (for example, S. Bochner [2]). More specifically, if $n = 2j + 1$, where j is integral, then the Fourier transform of the radial function f(R) is $\hat{f}(r) = \text{const}\,(d/rdr)^j \int_0^\infty f(R) \cos(Rr)\, dr$. In case $n = 2j + 2$ with j integral, then $\hat{f}(r) = \text{const}\,(d/dr)^j \int_0^\infty f(R)\, J_0(Rr)\, dr$.

Substitution of the indicated function f(R) leads to known integrals [1], giving in the odd-dimensional case

$$L_{t,\varepsilon}(\vec{x}) = \text{const}\left(\frac{d}{rdr}\right)^j K_0[m(r^2 + (it + \varepsilon)^{1/2}], \qquad r = |\vec{x}|,$$

where we employ the usual notation for the modified Bessel functions of the third kind. Now with use of the known property $(z^{-1}\, d/dz)^j K_0(z) = \text{const}\, z^{-j} K_j(z)$, the result is

$$L_{t,\varepsilon}(\vec{x}) = \text{const}\, z^{-j} K_j(z), \qquad z = [r^2 + (it + \varepsilon)^2]^{1/2}.$$

In the even-dimensional case, slightly different expressions lead ultimately to the identical expression for $L_{t,\varepsilon}(\vec{x})$, as noted by R. Jost [4].

Now the known asymptotic form for $K_j(z)$ for $|z|$ large is $K_j(z) = \text{const}\, z^{-1/2} e^{-z} (1 + O(|z|^{-1}))$ uniformly in the sector $|\arg z| < 3/2 - \delta$. This sector, however, contains all values of $z = (r^2 + (it + \varepsilon)^2)^{1/2}$ for $r > 0$ and $t > 0$, and for $t < 0$, the function in question is the complex conjugate of its value for $-t$. It results that $\|L_{t,\varepsilon}\|_\infty \leq \text{const}\, \sup_{r>0} |z|^{-n/2} e^{-\text{Re}(z)}$.

---

[4] In the work of A. R. Brodsky, it is indicated that a result quite analogous to Lemma 3 holds with C(t) given as essentially the L_∞ norm of the n-dimensional cosine transform of $\exp[it(m^2 + R^2)^{1/2}(m^2 + R^2)^{-a}$, where a is an adjustable constant to be chosen sufficiently large. But an estimate on the order of growth of this function for $|t| \to \infty$ is obtained which is best possible only for $m \geq 0$. In a number of applications, it is important that for $m > 0$, the rate of decay is a factor of $|t|^{1/2}$ more rapid than for $m = 0$.

Thus to establish Lemma 3 it suffices to show that

$$\sup_{r>0,t>0} |t/z|^{n/2} e^{-\mathrm{Re}(z)} < \infty.$$

Now the real part occurring in the exponential is always non-negative, since z is in the upper half-plane; thus $e^{-\mathrm{Re}(z)}$ remains bounded. Therefore unboundedness is possible only if

$$\lim \sup_{z/t \to 0} \frac{N}{D}$$

is infinite, where $N = e^{-\mathrm{Re}(z)}$ and $D = |z/t|^{n/2}$. It is easily seen that $z/t \to 0$ only if $t \to \infty$ and $r/t \to 1$. On setting $r/t = 1 - b$ and $\varepsilon/t = c$, and employing elementary estimates, $z/t = -2b + 2ic + 0(|b| + |c|)$ near $b = c = 0$. Since $\mathrm{Re}\ (-b + ic)^{1/2} = 1/2c[b + (b^2 + c^2)^{1/2}]^{-1}$, it follows that $\mathrm{Re}\ (z) \sim \mathrm{const}\ (b + (b^2 + c^2)^{1/2})^{-1/2} \to \infty$ as $b, c \to 0$. Since $e^{-A} \to 0$ as $A \to -\infty$ more rapidly than the inverse of any power, it suffices to show that for some positive exponent p, $(b + (b^2 + c^2)^{1/2})^p(b^2 + c^2)^{-n/2}$ is bounded as $b, c \to 0$, and indeed it is evident that for $p > n$, the lim sup of this expression as $b, c \to 0$ is 0.

End of proof of Lemma.[5]

The lemma shows in particular that all normalizable free wave functions ψ, $\Box\psi = m^2\psi$, whose Fourier transform is of compact support, have the uniform decay of the rapidity required for the application of Theorems 2 and 3, and we may state the following corollary.

Corollary 1. The hypotheses of Theorems 2 and 3 are satisfied in case the given wave function ϕ_0 has an infinitely differentiable Fourier transform of compact support, and if $F(\lambda)$ satisfies the indicated conditions near $\lambda = 0$ for some value of $a > 1 + (2/n)$.

---

[5]The fact that $\|\psi(t)\|_\infty = 0(|t|^{-3/2})$ when $n = 3$ and ψ has a Fourier transform which is C^∞ and of compact support has been a key point in the derivation by Ruelle of a fundamental result in the Haag-Wightman axiomatic field theory. A detailed account of the proof is given by A. Wightman [13]. Unfortunately, it is tacitly assumed in the proof that if $f(\lambda, u)$ is a continuous function, where $\lambda > 0$ and u ranges over a compact set and has a certain rate of decay for each u in certain regions, as $\lambda \to \infty$, then it will have at least the minimal rate of decay uniformly in u. It is difficult to see how to correct this gap without having the explicit bounds that would supersede the whole approach.

Proof: For any such wave function ϕ_0 we may write

$$\phi_0(\vec{x}, t) = \int \exp[-i(\vec{x} \cdot \vec{k} - tk_0)] \check{\phi}_0(k) \, dm(k),$$

where dm(k) is the element of Lorentz-invariant measure on the hyperboloid $\vec{k}^2 = k_0^2 - m^2$ over which the integration is performed, and $\check{\phi}_0(k)$ is C^∞ of compact support C. Now $dm(\vec{k})$ and the Euclidean measure in the dual to S have bounded densities relative to one another on C, and it follows that $\phi_0(\vec{x}, t)$ is for any time t the Fourier transform of a C^∞ function of compact support. The same is true of $\dot{\phi}_0(\vec{x}, t)$, since it is given by the same integral with $\check{\phi}_0(k)$ replaced by $ik_0\check{\phi}_0(k)$. The application of any C^∞ function of B to any function whose Fourier transform is of class C^∞ and of compact support gives another such function, and such function is necessarily integrable. Lemma 3 therefore implies that $\|\phi_0(\bullet, t)\|_\infty = 0(|t|^{-n/2})$. Taking then $f(t) = \text{const}\,|t|^{-n/2}$, the condition that $(f(t))^{-1} \int_{-\infty}^{t} f(s)^a \, ds \to 0$ is satisfied in case $|t|^{n/2} \int_{-\infty}^{t} s^{-an/2} \, ds \to 0$ as $t \to \infty$, which is found to be the case under the indicated condition.

End of proof of Corollary.

Remark 1. The proof of the preceding lemma is basically qualitative, avoiding the necessity of making an actual estimate for $\|L_{t,\varepsilon}\|_\infty$. Such an estimate can however be obtained [4] along lines similar to the foregoing in combination with the device of integration over ε. After multiplication by a suitable function of ε, it shows that the exponential function $e^{\varepsilon B}$ in Lemma 3 may be replaced by a certain power of B. It appears that still sharper results can be obtained by direct estimation of the integrals in question (work of S. Nelson).

Remark 2. For a general wave function ϕ of finite energy, $\|\phi(\bullet, t)\|_\infty$ may be infinite, so that Lemma 3 as it stands is certainly inapplicable to such general wave functions. However, some conclusions may be drawn regarding general wave functions, and there are possibilities for stronger results. We illustrate with the case n = 3.

Corollary 2. If ϕ is any finite energy solution of the (integral form of the) equation $\square\phi = m^2\phi$ in three space dimensions, then $\int |\phi(\vec{x}, t)|^p \, d\vec{x} \to 0$ for all p such that $2 < p \leq 6$ $(m > 0)$, or for $p = 6$ $(m = 0)$.

Proof: By the Soboleff inequality, in three dimensions, approximation in the energy norm implies approximation of the wave functions in the L_p norm for $2 \leq p \leq 6$. Hence, since the L_p norms decay for $p > 2$ in view of the boundedness of the L_2 norms and the decay of the L_∞ norms for the dense class of wave functions indicated in Corollary 1, this is true of all finite-energy wave functions. For the case $m = 0$, use is made here of the decay for this case as shown in [3].

End of proof.

For $n = 3$ and $p > 3$ (if $m > 0$, $p \geq 3$ is permitted), the integral over space-time $\int |\phi(\vec{x}, t)|^p \, d\vec{x} \, dt$ is finite, for any Klein-Gordon wave function whose Fourier transform is infinitely differentiable and of compact support. Corollary 2 provides weak evidence that this might be the case for all finite-energy wave functions, at least if p has the maximum value, $p = 6$; at any rate, there is no known evidence to the contrary.

Asymptotic behavior of solutions of nonlinear equations. In general, of course, the result of propagating to finite times by a given nonlinear equation a free wave function given at time $-\infty$, by means of Theorems 2 or 3, will be a solution of the nonlinear equation that exists only for sufficiently early times. In case it exists globally, as will for example be the case when the energy is positive definite and the interaction term is suitably continuous in the energy norm, it is, in addition, uncertain whether the solution has a well-defined asymptotic character for very late times or is in particular asymptotic to a solution of the free equation. This is, however, the case, for a general class of equations, of which those with power interactions leading to positive definite energies are typical, in 3 or more space dimensions.

Theorem 4. Any finite-energy global solution of the (integral form of the) equation

$$\Box\phi = m^2\phi + F(\phi)$$

is asymptotic as $t \to \infty$, in the weak topology relative to the energy as Banach norm, to a unique solution ϕ_1 of the equation

$$\Box\phi_1 = m^2\phi_1$$

if (a) the number of space dimensions is three or more (and if three, $m > 0$); (b) the energy and $\|F(\phi(\bullet, t))\|_1$ remain bounded as $t \to \infty$; (c) F is sufficiently regular that the mapping $[\phi, 0] \to [0, F(\phi)]$ is Lipschitzian on bounded sets, relative to the energy norm on the Cauchy data space.

Proof: As earlier, let $\Phi(t) = \phi(\bullet, t)$, and let $u(t) = [\Phi(t), \dot{\Phi}(t)]$. Then for each t, u(t) is in the Hilbert space H introduced earlier, in which the norm is $\|[f, g]\| = \|Bf\|^2 + \|g\|^2$, by virtue of the finite-energy character of ϕ. Let $W_0(t)$ be the one-parameter continuous orthogonal group indicated earlier, and set $v(t) = W_0(-t)u(t)$. Now $u(t)$ satisfies the equation

$$u(t) = W(t - t_0)u(t_0) + \int_{t_0}^{t} W_0(t - s)K(u(s))\, ds,$$

t_0 arbitrary, where $K[f, g] = [0, F(f)]$. This is the integral form of the indicated differential equation. It follows [9] that $v(t)$ satisfies the equation

$$v(t) - v(t') = \int_{t'}^{t} W_0(-s)K(u(s))\, ds$$

for all t and t'. Now let $\langle \cdot, \cdot \rangle$ indicate the inner product in $\underline{H}$ (that is, the energy inner product), and let w be an arbitrary fixed vector in $\underline{H}$. Then

$$\langle v(t) - v(t'), w \rangle = \int_{t'}^{t} \langle W_0(-s)K(u(s)), w \rangle\, ds$$

$$= \int_{t'}^{t} \langle K(u(s)), W_0(s)w \rangle\, ds.$$

Noting that $W_0(s)w$ is a solution of the free equation, say of the form $[\psi(s), \dot{\psi}(s)]$, it follows that

$$|\langle v(t) - v(t'), w \rangle| \leq \left| \int_{t'}^{t} \langle F(\Phi(s)), \dot{\psi}(s) \rangle_{L_2}\, ds \right|$$

$$\leq \left| \int_{t'}^{t} \|F(\Phi(s)\|_1 \, \|\dot{\psi}(s)\|_\infty \, ds \right|.$$

Now suppose that w has an infinitely differentiable Fourier transform of compact support. The solution $W_0(s)w$ of the free equation has the same property (in the dual to space-time, rather than to space), as does its first time derivative. Hence, by Lemma 2, $\|\dot{\psi}(s)\|_\infty$ is an integrable function of s. Making use of the assumption of boundeness of $\|F(\Phi(s)\|_1$, it follows that for such w, $\langle v(t) - v(t'), w \rangle \to 0$, as $t, t' \to \infty$.

Now the boundedness of the energy for the solution ϕ of the given nonlinear equation implies that u(t), and hence also v(t), are bounded in the Hilbert space $\underline{H}$. This space is separable, and a bounded set in it is therefore weakly sequentially compact. In particular, there exists a sequence $\{t_i\}$ tending to ∞ such that $\{v(t_i)\}$ is weakly convergent to some vector v_0. Now this vector is unique, since if $\{v(t_j')\}$ converges weakly to a vector v_1, where $\{t_j'\}$ is another sequence tending to ∞, then as we have just seen, $\langle v(t_i) - v(t_j'), w\rangle \to 0$, for all w of the type indicated earlier, as $i, j \to \infty$. This implies that $\langle v_0 - v_1, w\rangle = 0$, which in turn implies, by the density of the set of vectors w, that $v_0 - v_1 = 0$. Thus v(t) converges weakly, as $t \to \infty$, to a vector v_0.

Now let $u_0(t)$ be the solution of the free equation given by the equation $u_0(t) = W_0(t)v_0$. Then for any vector w in $\underline{H}$,

$$\langle u(t) - u_0(t), W_0(t)w\rangle = \langle W_0(-t)u(t) - W_0(-t)u_0(t), w\rangle$$

$$= \langle v(t) - v_0, w\rangle \to 0,$$

which means precisely that the solution u(t) of the nonlinear equation is asymptotic to the solution $u_0(t)$ of the free equation in the sense designated in Theorem 4. In other words, the required free solution $\phi_1(\vec{x}, t)$ is given by the stipulation that $\phi_1(\bullet, t)$ be the first component of $u_0(t)$.

It remains to show that ϕ_1 is the only free solution to which ϕ is asymptotic in the weak topology as $t \to \infty$. If ϕ is asymptotic also to the finite-energy solution ϕ_1 of the Klein-Gordon equation in the sense of Theorem 4, then $\phi_1 - \phi_2$ is asymptotic in the same sense to zero as $t \to \infty$. This means in particular that the energy inner product of the Cauchy data for $\phi_1 - \phi_2$ at any time with itself converges to zero as $t \to \infty$. The latter inner product is the energy of the free solution $\phi_1 - \phi_2$ at the time and is independent of the time; it can therefore converge to zero only if $\phi_1 = \phi_2$.

<u>End of proof.</u>

By combining Theorems 2 and 4, and by utilizing the energy bound to validate the L_1-boundedness required in Theorem 4, the existence of a well-defined dispersion operator follows for a general class of relativistic scalar equations in four-dimensional space-time.

<u>Corollary 3</u>. Let ϕ_0 be a solution of the equation $\Box\phi_0 = m^2\phi_0$ $(m > 0)$ in n-dimensional space-time (n = 3, 4, or 5), whose Fourier transform has compact support. Let F be a given function of a real variable of class C^1 such that (a) $F^{(j)}(\lambda) = 0(|\lambda|^{a+1-j})$ for j = 0, 1, 2, 3 with $a > 1 + 2n^{-1}$ near $\lambda = 0$; (b) as $\lambda \to \infty$, $F(\lambda) = 0(|\lambda|)$; (c) $\int_0^\lambda F(s)\,ds \geq 0$ and $|F(\lambda)| \leq$ const max $(\lambda^2, \int_0^\lambda F(s)\,ds)$.

Then, (1) there exists a unique solution of (the integral form of) the equation $\Box\phi = m^2\phi + F(\phi)$ which is strongly asymptotic to ϕ_0 in the energy norm, and which decays in the supremum norm at the rate $0(|t|^{-n/2})$ as $t \to -\infty$; (2) ϕ is in turn weakly asymptotic in the energy norm to a unique solution ϕ_1 of finite energy of the (integral form of the) equation $\Box\phi_1 = m^2\phi_1$.

Proof: The existence of the solution ϕ satisfying condition 1 of the conclusion is a special case of Corollary 1. The uniqueness was stated earlier under the assumption that $\Phi(t)$ is bounded in L_∞ by $(1 + \varepsilon)f(t)$, where $f(t)$ is as given in Theorem 1, but with the present assumptions on $F(\lambda)$, the uniqueness proof is equally applicable under the assumption that $\|\Phi(t)\|_\infty \leq$ const $F(t)$. Conclusion 2 then results from Theorem 4, on verification of hypotheses b and c of that theorem. Concerning b, the conservation of energy for the nonlinear equation asserts that

$$\|B\Phi(t)\|_2^2 + \|\dot{\Phi}(t)\|_2^2 + E(\Phi(t)) = \text{const}$$

where

$$E(\Phi(t)) = \int H(\phi(\vec{x}, t))\, d\vec{x}, \qquad H(\lambda) = \int_0^\lambda F(s)\, ds.$$

Now

$$\begin{aligned}\|F(\phi(\bullet, t))\|_1 &= \int |F(\phi(\vec{x}, t))|\, d\vec{x} \\ &\leq \text{const} \int \max\,\{\phi(\vec{x}, t)^2,\ H[\phi(\vec{x}, t)]\}\, d\vec{x} \\ &\leq \text{const} \int \phi(\vec{x}, t)^2\, d\vec{x} + \int H[\phi(\vec{x}, t)]\, d\vec{x}.\end{aligned}$$

From the indicated conservation law, the last expression is evidently bounded as a function of t. Regarding condition c, the semi-Lipschitzian character of the indicated mapping follows directly from the Soboleff inequalities from the assumption on the growth of $F(\lambda)$ for $|\lambda| \to \infty$ [9]. End of proof.

An immediate consequence is the following corollary:

Corollary 4. The dispersion operator exists in the sense indicated in Theorem 4 for the equation: $\Box\phi = m^2\phi + g\phi^3$ $(m > 0,\ g > 0)$ in four-dimensional space-time.

Traditionally, it has been customary to emphasize the class of local relativistic interactions that are expressible in terms of simple polynomials in the fields in question. In the case of a scalar field, the power interactions $F(\lambda) = g\lambda^p$ are the simplest, and these almost exclusively among nonlinear relativistic scalar equations have been considered in the body of heuristic developments associated with relativistic physical theory. The existence part of Corollary 4 is essentially valid for these equations. The uniqueness part in conclusion 1 of Corollary 3 is, however, uncertain; the uniqueness in conclusion 2 remains valid as it is essentially a fact concerning free solutions. The main change required is the sense in which "solution of the nonlinear equation" and "weak convergence" are understood. In general, for a finite-energy function $\phi(\vec{x}, t)$, the function $\phi(\vec{x}, t)^p$ need not even be locally integrable for any fixed time; the condition c of Theorem 4 does not hold. There is nevertheless a natural weak sense in which to formulate the notion of solution [10].

Corollary 5. Let ϕ_0 be a solution of the equation $\Box\phi_0 = m^2\phi_0$ in (n + 1)-dimensional space time, with $n \geq 3$, whose Fourier transform has compact support. Let p be an odd integer; in case $m = 0$ and $n = 3$, suppose also that $p > 3$. Suppose that $g > 0$. Then: (1) there exists a finite-energy weak solution ϕ, relative to the test functions dual to the finite-energy data, of the (integral form of the) equation $\Box\phi = m^2\phi + g\phi^p$, which as $t \to \infty$ is strongly asymptotic to ϕ_0 in the energy norm and decays in the supremum norm at the rate $0(|t|^{-n/2})$ (ϕ is unique in the region $t < t_0$, for some t_0); (2) ϕ is in turn weakly asymptotic (relative to the energy inner product) as $t \to \infty$ to a unique solution ϕ_1 of the (integral form of the) equation $\Box\phi_1 = m^2\phi_1$.

Proof: We first refer to Reference [10] for a detailed account of the weak solutions in question, and recall only that, with the notation $u(t) = [\Phi(t), \dot{\Phi}(t)]$ employed earlier, $K(u)$ defined as $[0, g\Phi^p]$ for $u = [\Phi, \psi]$, and $W_0(t)$ as earlier, a weak solution of the integrated form of the equation $\Box\phi = m^2\phi + g\phi^p$ may be defined as a function $u(t)$ with values in the space of finite-energy Cauchy data $[\Phi, \psi]$ for which $\psi \in L_{p+1}$. This means precisely that the total conserved energy should be finite, such that for any vector $v = [\Phi, \psi]$ in the space of finite-energy data for which $\psi \in L_{(p+1)/p}$ (that is, the space conjugate to L_{p+1}), the equation

$$\langle u(t), v\rangle = \langle W_0(t - t_0)u_0, v\rangle + \int_{t_0}^{t} \langle K(u(s)),\ W_0(s - t)v\rangle\, ds \qquad (9)$$

is valid. Here, $\langle f, g\rangle$ is defined as $\int fg\, d\vec{x}$ for arbitrary functions f and g; note that the expression $W_0(t - s)K(u(s))$, used earlier, does not occur, and indeed has no definite meaning, since K is an unbounded operator having values outside the domain $W_0(t-s)$. It is avoided by the use of duality. It is known that a solution to Equation 9 exists such that $\langle u(t), v\rangle$ is a differentiable function of t for all v (when the initial data u_0 and t_0 are given), but it is not known whether the solution is unique.

Conclusion 1 of Corollary 5 follows directly from Theorems 2 and 3, apart from the global existence of the solution, already cited. To establish conclusion 2, consider first the case of a test function represented by a free solution whose Fourier transform is of class C^∞ and of compact support, and follow the lines of the proof of Theorem 4. The free solution $y_0(t)$ may be assumed to have the form $y_0(t) = W_0(t)y$. Substitution in Equation 9 with $t_0 = 0$ shows that for an arbitrary test vector z (letting $v = W_0(t)z$),

$$\langle u(t), W_0(t)z\rangle = \langle W_0(t)y, W_0(t)z\rangle + \int_0^t \langle K(u(s)), W_0(s)z\rangle \, ds.$$

Defining $v(t) = W_0(-t)u(t)$ gives the result

$$\langle v(t) - v(t'), z\rangle = \int_t^{t'} \langle K(u(s)), W_0(s)z\rangle \, ds.$$

Therefore

$$|\langle v(t) - v(t'), z\rangle| \le \left| \int_{t'}^{t} \|F(\Phi(s))\|_1 \, \|W_0(s)z\|_\infty \, ds \right|.$$

Since the free solution $y_0(t)$ has been assumed to correspond to a free wave function $\phi(\vec{x}, t)$ whose Fourier transform has compact support, $\|W_0(s)z\|_\infty = 0(|s|^{-n/2})$; it results that $\langle v(t) - v(t'), z\rangle \to 0$ as $t, t' \to \infty$. Because the v(t) are bounded in the energy norm by the orthogonality of the $W_0(t)$ on $\underline{H}$ and the boundedness of the energy of the u(t), it follows, as in the proof of Theorem 4, that v(t) converges weakly in the energy norm to a vector v_0 in $\underline{H}$ as $t \to \infty$.

This means that the solution u(t) is asymptotic to the free solution $W_0(t)v_0$ in the sense indicated in Corollary 5. That v_0 is the only vector in $\underline{H}$ for which this is true follows by the identical argument with that employed to establish uniqueness in the proof of Theorem 4. End of proof.

3. Conclusion

At this point we could readily deal with a number of relevant matters, such as the relativistic invariance of the forward-wave and dispersion operators, the C^∞ character of these operators (in the sense of Fréchet-Gateau), relative to certain Banach norms on the spaces in question. We are also in a position to begin the construction of a temporally invariant probability measure in the solution manifold of the nonlinear differential equations considered here. This construction and the theory of the resulting measures will be given in another article.

A number of significant open questions emerge from the foregoing developments concerning nonlinear relativistic equations in the large, which we list with some comments in the hope that they may find rapid solution.

1. Strong asymptotic convergence, for $t \to \infty$. There is an evident asymmetry between the topologies involved in the asymptotic convergence of the solution of the nonlinear wave equation to a solution of the linear one as $t \to -\infty$ on the one hand and $t \to \infty$ on the other. Although the weak convergence corresponds more closely than the strong convergence to what is actually physically measured, it remains to show that the asymptotic free solution in the sense of weak convergence uniquely determines the solution of the nonlinear equation. Physically it would be rather shocking if this were not the case, at least for the solutions of the nonlinear equation obtained by propagation from time $-\infty$ of smooth free solutions. This question is technically closely related to the question of

2. Decay on L_∞ of nonlinear solutions. It is plausible that a solution of an equation such as $\Box\phi = m^2\phi + g\phi^3$ in $(n + 1)$-dimensional space-time, at least one which is asymptotic for $t \to -\infty$ to a free solution whose Fourier transform is C^∞ and of compact support, for $t \to \infty$ should satisfy also the estimate $\|\Phi(t)\|_\infty = 0(|t|^{-n/2})$ or some effective generalization of this estimate.

3. Analogue of the Floquet-Liapounoff theory for the first-order variational equations. The question of the existence of an extension of the symplectic structure in the solution manifold to a Kählerian structure, which is likewise invariant under the Lorentz group and the S-operator, is closely connected with the development of an analogue to the Floquet-Liapounoff theory giving conditions for the stability of the solutions of a second-order ordinary differential equation with periodic coefficients in the case of second-order hyperbolic equations whose coefficients are asymptotically constant for $t \to \pm\infty$, for example, the equation $\Box\lambda = m^2\lambda + V(\vec{x}, t)\lambda$, where $V(\vec{x}, t)$ is a given nonnegative function tending suitably to zero as $|t| \to \infty$.

4. Extension of existence and dispersion theory to equations of indefinite energy. The equations of quantum electrodynamics

are, of course, of great interest in this connection, as well as of particular difficulty.

5. Uniqueness and dispersion theory for weak solutions of singularly nonlinear relativistic equations. We refer to equations whose nonlinear term is not a continuous function of the wave function relative to the energy norm. For example, the equations $\square\phi = m^2\phi + g\phi^p$ with $p > 3$, in a space-time of dimension ≥ 4. It is plausible that uniqueness should be valid at least for solutions asymptotic in the sense of Theorems 2 and 3 to regular free solutions as $t \to -\infty$. One would, in fact, expect such solutions to remain strong for all time. On the other hand, it is plausible that there should be difficulties in this regard for highly singular equations. For example, an equation of the form $\square\phi = m^2\phi + g \exp[\phi^4]\phi^3$ can probably be treated to some extent by the method of Reference 10, and Theorems 2 and 3 are applicable to it. It would not be surprising if the dispersion operator for the equation, whose existence should follow along the lines of the proof of Corollary 5 from the existence of global solutions to the equation for prescribed finite-energy data, were identically zero. An explicit example of this would be of physical interest as providing a model for the (apparent) destruction of energy in which the interaction is nevertheless local and relativistic, and for which the energy is conserved for all finite times (or on reversing the direction of time, for the apparent creation of energy).

References

1. Bateman, H., Higher Transcendental Functions, ed. A. Erdelyi, MacGraw-Hill Book Company, Inc., New York, 1953, Vol. 2.

2. Bochner, S., Lectures on Fourier Integrals, Princeton University Press, Princeton, N.J., 1959, p. 172.

3. Brodsky, A. R., "Asymptotic Decay of Solutions to the Relativistic Wave Equation and the Existence of Scattering for Certain Nonlinear Hyperbolic Equations," Doctoral dissertation, Department of Mathematics, M.I.T., Cambridge, Mass., 1964.

4. Jost, R., Über das zeitliche Verhalten von glatten Lösungen der Klein-Gordon Gleichung, Preprint, received.

5. Segal, I. E., "Foundations of the Theory of Dynamical Systems of Infinitely Many Degrees of Freedom," Kgl. Danske Videnskab Selskab, Mat.-fys. Medd., 31, No. 12, 1 (1959).

6. Segal, I. E., "Quantization of Nonlinear Systems," J. Math. Phys., 1, 468 (1960).

7. Segal, I. E., Can. J. Math., 13, 1 (1961).

8. Segal, I. E., Illinois J. Math., 6, 500 (1962).

9. Segal, I. E., "Non-linear Semi-groups," Ann. Math., 78, 339 (1963).

10. Segal, I. E., "The Global Cauchy Problem for a Relativistic Scalar Field with Power Interaction," Bull. Soc. Math. France, 91, 129 (1963).

11. Segal, I. E., Mathematical Problems of Relativistic Physics, with Appendix, "Group Representations," by G. W. Mackey American Mathematical Society, Providence, R.I., 1963.

12. Segal, I. E., "Explicit Formal Construction of Non-linear Quantum Fields," J. Math. Phys., 5, 269 (1964).

13. Wightman, A., "Recent Achievements of Axiomatic Field Theory," in Theoretical Physics, International Atomic Energy Agency, Vienna, 1963, pp. 46-49.

Chapter 9

SPONTANEOUS BREAKDOWN OF SYMMETRY

R. F. Streater

Summary

The idea of a spontaneous breakdown of symmetry is formulated within the Haag-Araki framework of quantum field theory; it is argued that this formulation includes the ideas heuristically put forward in the usual Lagrangian theories.

It is proved that there can be no spontâneous breakdown of symmetry in a free boson field of nonzero mass. It is also proved that in any reasonable theory a one-parameter group of automorphisms cannot cause any mass splitting between states, unless the theory contains other states with arbitrarily small and definite quantum numbers.

Therefore the notion of spontaneous breakdown of symmetry must be abandoned as the explanation of the violations of isotopic spin symmetry that are observed in nature.

1. Introduction

Recently a great deal of progress has been made in understanding the general structure of quantum field theory using the algebraic formulation introduced by Haag [15; 18] and developed by Araki [2; 3] and others [5]. The results are, of necessity, entirely general, such as the asymptotic condition [2] and the analysis of spin and statistics by Borchers [6]. In this work, it is assumed that the observables form a C*-algebra $\mathscr{A}$, that is, a concrete Banach algebra of operators on a Hilbert space $\mathscr{H}$. Further structure is added to the system $(\mathscr{H}, \mathscr{A})$ in the form of axioms; these represent physical laws.

More recently, Haag and Kastler [17] have taken the process of abstraction even further, and, following to some extent the lines advocated by Segal [26], suggest that only the properties of $\mathscr{A}$ that are algebraically invariant should have true physical meaning. While this point of view is very appealing, it has practical disadvantages;

for many of the conditions put on the system ($\mathscr{H}$, $\mathscr{A}$) are most conveniently expressed in a way that is representation dependent; in particular, the condition that the automorphism of $\mathscr{A}$ induced by a space-time translation $x^\mu \to x^\mu + a^\mu$ should be represented by a unitary operator U(a) in $\mathscr{H}$ is not a purely algebraic property. This means that there exist representations of $\mathscr{A}$ in which the translation group of automorphisms cannot be expressed as a unitary transformation $S \to U(a)\, SU(a)^{-1}$. In such a representation the generators of the group, the energy-momentum vector, would not exist. Even among representations in which the energy exists, the energy spectrum might differ from one to the other, since the translations are not elements of $\mathscr{A}$. Thus, the physically important fact that the energy is positive is certainly not an algebraic invariant.

Naturally, the statement, that there exists a representation of $\mathscr{A}$ fulfilling the spectrum condition, is invariant under isomorphism, since any representation of $\mathscr{A}$ is also a representation of any algebra isomorphic to $\mathscr{A}$. Therefore, this is a property of the abstract algebra $\mathscr{A}$ and the automorphism induced by translations. But no one has succeeded in isolating this algebraic property in a useful form that does not work in a particular representation. The recent attempt by Doplicher [8] actually fails; the point is that he did not succeed in giving a meaning to the integration of operator-valued functions like $S(a) \equiv U(a)\, SU(a)^{-1}$ for $S \in \mathscr{A}$, without working in a particular representation.

Most of the results of the theory depend on the assumption that there exists a representation with positive energy, and are derived in that representation. If there is only one such representation and we take this representation as a privileged one, then we return to the earlier concrete form of the theory of Haag and Araki. However, in realistic theories, there are many representations with positive energy, which, as explained by Haag and Kastler [17], correspond to the various superselection sectors, that is, to Hilbert spaces of states with different charge.

Thus, for physical reasons, we expect there to be a number of representations with positive energy; but we might hope that there is only one representation with positive energy and a vacuum state. However, the author has shown [31] that this is not true for the free boson field of zero mass, and that many inequivalent representations exist, all with the same mass spectrum. The other representations are obtained from the Fock representation by a "broken symmetry transformation," and can only happen in the case of zero mass. This occurrence of zero mass states is related to the Goldstone theorem, of which perfectly sound proofs exist in the physics literature [9; 30], if one admits various technical hypotheses. Thus, apart from cases where zero-mass particles occur, we might expect there to be a unique representation with unique vacuum and positive energy.

The question of the uniqueness of the representation with vacuum and positive energy was raised by Segal in the mathematics literature [27], but can be seen also in the earlier papers of Coester and Haag [7] and Araki [1]. In these papers the question takes the form: given a Hamiltonian H as a function of the canonical variables, is there a unique representation of the canonical commutation relations that is consistent with H, in the sense that H is self-adjoint, and positive in this representation? There are two contributions that deserve mention. Segal proves [27] for the free field,[1] that there is a unique representation with positive energy and vacuum state $\rangle_0$, such that the vacuum functional $\langle e^{i\phi(f)}\rangle_0$ is continuous in the test function f in a certain Hilbert space topology. This continuity condition is violated by the non-Fock vacua of the free Bose field of zero mass (this is proved in Reference 31). Thus while Segal's proof provides a start to the problem, the continuity condition may be so strong as to exclude just the representations we are looking for in a broken symmetry theory.

The other general result is due to Borchers [5]. This author is not interested in all representations of $\mathscr{A}$ but only in those related to each other by what may be called <u>strong local equivalence</u>. This notion is rather stronger than that of local unitary equivalence in the sense of Misra [24]. Borchers' result says, given a representation of $\mathscr{A}$ with a unique vacuum and positive energy, there is no other representation, in the <u>strong</u> local equivalence class, with a vacuum and positive energy. (In his paper [5] he inadvertently states the theorems in terms of local unitary equivalence but uses strong local equivalence in the proofs.)

Here again, this is only a partial result; one would like to have uniqueness of the vacuum representation in the class of locally equivalent theories, but this is not true in general: the infinity of representations of the mass-zero free field [31] are locally equivalent (but not strongly locally equivalent) to each other and to the Fock representation, and all have positive energy. A related result was given by Guénin and Velo [10] and was also found by Misra [25], whose version we give. If we are given an irreducible representation of $\mathscr{A}$ with a vacuum state Ψ_0, and if $\omega: S \to \omega(S)$ is a translation-invariant functional with the property: $S \to 1$ weakly $\Rightarrow$ $\omega(S) \to 1$, then $\omega(S) = (\Psi_0, S\Psi_0)$. The vacuum functionals given in Reference 31 are easily seen not to satisfy this continuity condition, which is rather strong for applications.

The present paper is organized as follows. In Section 2 we formulate the idea of spontaneously broken symmetry and show the connection with the question of the existence of inequivalent repre-

---

[1] It should be pointed out that the C*-algebra of the free field used by Segal differs from that common in the physics literature, for example in Reference 31.

sentations having the same representation of translations. In Section 3 we prove that for the free field with nonzero mass there is no symmetry that is spontaneously broken. In Section 4 we prove the generalization of Goldstone's theorem recently announced [30], namely, that if a symmetry $\psi_1 \to \psi_2$ is spontaneously broken, then either the fields ψ_1 and ψ_2 have the same mass, or there are states in the theory with arbitrarily small mass having the quantum numbers of $\psi_2^*\psi_1$. In Section 5 it is shown how the hypotheses used in the proof of the theorem of Section 4 may be derived from the assumptions usually made in Wightman theory. In Section 6 we apply the theorem to prove that the breakdown of isotopic spin symmetry is not of the spontaneous type.

2. Spontaneously Broken Symmetry

We define a Haag field as in the paper of Borchers [5]. A natura way to study the symmetries of a quantum field would be to conside the group of automorphisms of the algebra of observables $\mathscr{A}$. How ever, apart from space-time symmetries, the symmetries of inter est, like isotopic spin SU_3, and so forth, do not map the observable into themselves; they usually mix fields with different superselection quantum numbers like charge, and so forth. Thus, in practice we should consider automorphisms of the field algebra $\mathscr{F}$ associate with $\mathscr{A}$.

We assume that $\mathscr{A}$ has a representation with a vacuum, and a series of other representations strongly locally equivalent. We co sider the (reducible) representation of $\mathscr{A}$ formed from the direct sum of these representations. Let $\mathscr{H}$ be the resulting Hilbert spac The field algebra $\mathscr{F}$ acts in $\mathscr{H}$ irreducibly, and contains $\mathscr{A}$ as a su algebra.

We are not concerned with the most general assumptions [6] under which this setup can be established; it may be assumed "on physical grounds." For each open region $\mathscr{O}$ of space-time, an automorphism g: $\mathscr{F} \to \mathscr{F}$ defines by restriction a mapping of $\mathscr{F}(\mathscr{O})$ into $\mathscr{F}$, where $\mathscr{F}(\mathscr{O})$ is the local von Neumann algebra generated by the fields in $\mathscr{O}$. However, it is unreasonable to expect that all these automorphisms correspond to symmetries seen in nature. In this paper we shall consider those automorphisms g: $\mathscr{F} \to \mathscr{F}$ satisfying the following two conditions:

1. The automorphism g commutes with space-time translation.
2. For each bounded open set $\mathscr{O}$ there exists a unitary operator $U(\mathscr{O})$ such that

$$\psi_g = U(\mathscr{O})\psi U(\mathscr{O})^{-1} \text{ for } \psi \in \mathscr{F}(\mathscr{O}),$$

where $\psi \to \psi_g$ is the action of g on an element $\psi \in \mathscr{F}$.

We say the symmetry is spontaneously broken if there does not exist an operator U such that $\psi_g = U\psi U^{-1}$ for all $\psi \in \mathscr{F}$.

In a previous paper [29] we considered several other conditions on an automorphism in order for it to be a symmetry of interest. The image $\mathscr{F}\{(\mathscr{O})\}_g$ under g of a local ring system $\mathscr{F}\{(\mathscr{O})\}$ is clearly a local ring system; it is natural to require that it is local relative to the original system; that is, if $\mathscr{O}$ and $\mathscr{O}_1$ are spacelike separated, then $\mathscr{F}(\mathscr{O})_g \subset \mathscr{F}(\mathscr{O}_1)'$ (the commutant of $\mathscr{F}(\mathscr{O}_1)$). Then we would say that $\mathscr{F}\{(\mathscr{O})\}_g$ is in the Borchers class of $\mathscr{F}(\mathscr{O})$, by analogy with the successful notion introduced in field theory (see Reference 4). It is natural to impose an even stronger condition, namely,

3. The automorphism g maps each $\mathscr{F}(\mathscr{O})$ onto itself.

If an automorphism satisfies conditions 1, 2, and 3, it is called an "internal" symmetry.

The mapping $\psi \to \psi_g$ provides a representation of $\mathscr{F}$ in $\mathscr{H}$, which need not be strongly locally equivalent to the given one. The requirement 1 that g commutes with the translations is actually equivalent to the requirement that the two representations $\mathscr{F}$ and $\mathscr{F}_g$ have the same representation of the translation group [31], a necessary result if the local ring systems $\mathscr{F}\{(\mathscr{O})\}$ and $\mathscr{F}\{(\mathscr{O})\}_g$ are to belong to the same Borchers class.

Condition 1 may also be expressed as the commutativity of the diagram

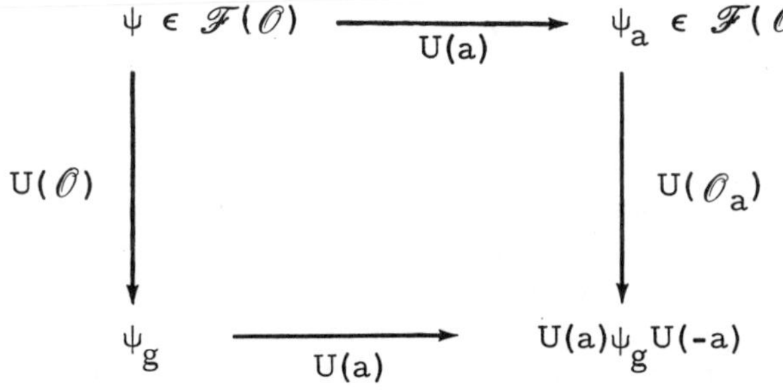

so that $U(a)U(\mathscr{O})U(-a)$ serves the same purpose as $U(\mathscr{O}_a)$ in implementing the automorphism g for the algebra $\mathscr{F}(\mathscr{O}_a)$. Naturally, the operator $U(\mathscr{O})$ in condition 3 is not all unique.

The two representations $\mathscr{F}$ and $\mathscr{F}_g$ are unitary equivalent if and only if the symmetry is not broken. Since both have positive energy, we see the relevance of the uniqueness, or otherwise, of representations with positive energy to the question of broken symmetry. Using the Gelfand-Segal construction connecting representations with positive linear functionals, we see that the functionals $\omega: \psi \to (\Psi_0, \psi\Psi_0)$ and $\omega_g: \psi \to (\Psi_0, \psi_g \Psi_0)$ are equal if and only if g is unitarily implementable. Since both ω and ω_g are invariant under translations, we see the relevance of the question of the uniqueness of translationally invariant states on $\mathscr{F}$. It should be said that it has not been proved that every invariant positive linear functional $\Omega: \psi \rightarrow \Omega(\psi)$ on $\mathscr{F}$, leading to a theory with positive energy, is of the form $\Omega(\psi) = \omega(\psi_g)$ for some automorphism g. If an automorphism g does not commute with the time translations, then it corresponds (in Lagrangian field theory) to a transformation under which the Lagrangian or equations of motion are not invariant. In this case the symmetry is explicitly, not spontaneously, broken.

Condition 2, the local unitary implementability of g, is not a very strong requirement. It ought to be possible to prove it from the other axioms [24]. In a Lagrangian field theory with a symmetry, the corresponding conserved current leads to the existence of the operators $U(\mathcal{O})$ (see later). Since the existence of the conserved currents is either derived heuristically, or assumed, our conditions 1, 2, and 3 are designed to cover all the examples of spontaneously broken symmetry discussed so far.[2]

We have not imposed the condition that g commutes with the Lorentz group. While this is a natural requirement, the generalization obtained by omitting it allows the interesting case where there is a vector, tensor, and so forth, each component of which is conserved and which generates a group of automorphisms of $\mathscr{F}$. The total symmetry group would then be a semidirect product of the Poincare group with the internal group, as first suggested by Michel, and Condition 3 would not hold.

3. Discussion of the Free Field Theory

In a free field theory it is possible to construct an infinite number of conserved currents, which are Wick-ordered products in the field, and therefore local. For the free electromagnetic field, some of these have been given by D. M. Lipkin [23], and the complete list of those quadratic in the fields was found by T. W. B. Kibble [21]. The author has been able to find others which are not quadratic in the field and its derivatives but which are of any chosen degree.

The divergence of such a current vanishes in virtue of the Klein-Gordon equation or other free equation of motion, and so we do not expect such currents to be conserved in the case of interacting fields. Nevertheless, from the point of view of algebraic quantum field theory, it is interesting to see if these currents correspond to any conserved quantities, which would formally be written as integrals of the time components over a spacelike surface. Such an integral could act as a generator for a one-parameter contin-

[2]For a good review, see the contribution of G. S. Guralnik [12] and two of his papers [11]. For the nonrelativistic formulation, see R. Haag [16], R. Lange [22], and G. S. Guralnik, C. R. Hagen, and T. W. B. Kibble [13].

uous group of automorphisms of the field algebra $\mathscr{F}$, at least heuristically. This group will commute with the Poincaré group (if $j^{\mu}(x)$ has no vector indices besides μ) or will behave as a translation-invariant tensor (if $j^{\mu}(x)$ carries other tensor indices). In the latter case, condition 3 will not hold.[3]

Naturally, there are problems of rigor; these are discussed in Section 5.

It might be that the space integrals of some of these currents, especially those formed from the higher powers of the field, diverge. This would be a typical broken symmetry situation, since the corresponding automorphism of $\mathscr{F}$ would not be unitarily implementable, and we could set up an inequivalent representation of the free field with nonzero mass and positive energy. In this section we prove that this never happens; that is, any representation of the free field locally equivalent to the Fock representation, and with the same representation of the translation group, is globally equivalent to the Fock representation unless the mass is zero. In those cases where the current $j^{\mu}(x)$ is related to the energy momentum tensor density, the corresponding automorphism is a space-time translation or a Lorentz transformation. These transformations naturally do not map each local algebra $R(\mathscr{O})$ into itself but into the algebra corresponding to the transformed region of space-time. In many cases where the automorphism corresponding to the current is not related to space-time motions, the automorphism reduces to the identity. This must always be the case for all automorphisms mapping each $R(\mathscr{O})$ into itself. This is a corollary of Theorem 1, which we now give; for the notation used here see [32] which also contains other material.

Theorem 1. Suppose $\{\mathscr{H}_1, U_1(a, \Lambda), \phi_1(x)\}$ is a free Wightman field with domain D, and $\{\mathscr{H}_2, U_2(a), \phi_2(x)\}$ is a Wightman field such that

1. $U_1(a, 1)$ and $U_2(a)$ are unitary equivalent: $U_2(a) = VU_1(a, 1)V^{-1}$.
2. for each bounded region $\mathscr{O}$ there exists a unitary operator $U(\mathscr{O}): \mathscr{H}_1 \to \mathscr{H}_2$ such that $U(\mathscr{O})^{-1}VD \subset D$ and $\phi_2(x) = U(\mathscr{O})\phi_1(x)U(\mathscr{O})^{-1}$, for all $x \in \mathscr{O}$.

Then $\phi_2(x)$ is a free Wightman field with the same mass m if $m \neq 0$. If $m = 0$, $\phi_2(x)$ may differ from a free field by a constant.

Proof: Clearly $V\Psi_{10} = \Psi_{20} \in \mathscr{H}_2$ is invariant under translations, and $U^{-1}(\mathscr{O})\Psi_{20}$ is in the domain of $\phi_1(f)$; that is, Ψ_{20} is in the domain of $\phi_2(f)$. Then

[3]It is a strange fact of life [29] that the exponential of a space integral of a current might move the local ring system from region to region even though the current is local.

$$(\Psi_{20}, \phi_2(x)\phi_2(y)\Psi_{20}) = F(x, y)$$

is a translation invariant distribution and so depends on x - y only. It is of positive type, and so is tempered. Since the representations $U_1(a, 1)$ and $U_2(a)$ are unitary equivalent, they have the same mass spectrum (that is, in the forward cone), so the Fourier transform of $F(x - y)$, say $\widetilde{F}(p)$, has its support in the set $\{p = 0\}$ or $\{p^2 = m^2, p^0 > 0\}$ or $\{p^2 \geq 4m^2, p^0 > 0\}$. On the other hand, if x and $y \in \mathscr{O}$

$$(\Psi_{20}, [\phi_2(x), \phi_2(y)]\Psi_{20}) = (\Psi_{20}, U(\mathscr{O})[\phi_1(x), \phi_1(y)]U^{-1}(\mathscr{O})\Psi_{20})$$

$$= \Delta(x - y; m).$$

But $\mathscr{O}$ is arbitrary, showing that this holds for all x and y. Since $U_1(a, 1)$ and $U_2(a)$ are unitary equivalent, Ψ_{20} is the only translation invariant state in $\mathscr{H}_2$.

Identifying the positive energy part of the last equation, we get, if $m > 0$,

$$(\Psi_{20}, \phi_2(x)\phi_2(y)\Psi_{20}) = \Delta^+(x - y; m) + \eta^2,$$

where $\eta = (\Psi_{20}, \phi_2(x)\Psi_{20})$. But we know that $\phi_1((\Box + m^2)f) = 0$, and $\phi_2((\Box + m^2)f) = U(\mathscr{O})\phi_1((\Box + m^2)f)U(\mathscr{O})^{-1}$ if $f = 0$ outside $\mathscr{O}$. Therefore, $\phi_2(x)$ vanishes on test functions of the form $(\Box + m^2)f$, $f \in \mathscr{D}(\mathscr{O})$. This implies that $\eta = 0$. We now apply a theorem of Jost [20] to prove that the Wightman functions of $\phi_2(x)$ are those of the free field of mass m, and so by the reconstruction theorem [33] $\phi_2(x)$ is the free field of mass m.

If $m = 0$, we can no longer split off the support of $\widetilde{F}(p)$ into a term $p = 0$ coming from the vacuum intermediate state, and the rest. But we may identify

$$(\Psi_{20}, \phi_2(p)\phi_2(q)\Psi_{20}) - (\Psi_{10}, \phi_1(p)\phi_1(q)\Psi_{10})$$

with a distribution having support at the origin, that is, a finite sum of derivatives of $\eta^2\delta^4(p)\delta^4(q)$. The positive-definite condition forces η to be real, and no derivatives to occur. Thus

$$(\Psi_{20}, \phi_2(x)\phi_2(y)\Psi_{20}) = \Delta^+(x - y; 0) + \eta^2,$$

and the same argument as before shows that $\phi_2(x) = \phi_2'(x) + \eta$, where $\phi_2'(x)$ is a free field of zero mass. This proves the theorem.

It follows from this that any automorphism of the free field algebra ($m \neq 0$) satisfying conditions 1 and 2 must be unitarily implementable if the domain condition holds. This will always be the case for operators $U(\mathcal{O})$ built out of Wick polynomials in the free field. Thus we cannot use the local conserved currents of the free field to generate inequivalent representations if $m \neq 0$, and if $m = 0$ the only ones are those already found [31].

It follows from the theorem that any automorphism of the free field satisfying conditions 1, 2, and 3, is the trivial one, the identity. For the transformed field $\phi_2(x)$ will be in the Borchers class of $\phi_1(x)$, and $\phi_1(x)$ is the only field in this class satisfying $(\Box + m^2)\phi(x) = 0$, if $\phi_1(x)$ is irreducible. Naturally, nontrivial "isotopic spin" transformations exist in a theory of two free fields of the same mass; the transformation is generated by the well-known conserved current.

We should remark that this theorem is not a form of Haag's theorem [14; 19] since there the unitary operator giving equivalence of ϕ_1 and ϕ_2 may be time-dependent (that is, does not commute with time translations). In fact, it remains an interesting question whether or not there exist representations of the canonical commutation relations (C-C-R's) which, at each fixed time, are unitary equivalent to the Fock representation in any finite volume, and such that the field defines a relativistic Haag ring. (Nonrelativistic theories locally equivalent to the Fock representation of the C-C-R's are expected to exist; they are used to describe a many-body system.)

4. Generalized Goldstone's Theorem

In this section we prove that spontaneous breakdown of a continuous symmetry group cannot be responsible for the mass-differences observed in nature. An outline of the proof was published recently in Physical Review Letters [30].

Consider a Haag field with global algebra $\mathscr{A}(M)$, and let $\mathscr{F}(M)$ be the global algebra of fields generated by the representations of $\mathscr{A}$, as outlined earlier. The representations under consideration are strongly locally equivalent to the vacuum representation. We are going to consider two fields ψ_1 and ψ_2 in $\mathscr{F}$ which, acting on the vacuum, produce states in the coherent subspaces $\mathscr{H}_1$ and $\mathscr{H}_2$ of $\mathscr{H}$. In the construction of Borchers, ψ_1 and ψ_2 can be chosen to be unitary and localized in any given open set $\mathcal{O}$. Suppose that the lowest point on the mass spectrum of states in $\mathscr{H}_1$ is m_1, and the lowest point on the mass spectrum of states in $\mathscr{H}_2$ is m_2, where $m_2 > m_1 \geq 0$. Let us assume that $m_0 > 0$ is a lower bound for states with the quantum numbers of the fields $\psi_2^*\psi_1$. Let $\Psi \in \mathscr{H}_1$ be a state with maximum energy less than m_2 and whose energy is contained in a set Δ of radius less than $m_0/2$. Let $\psi_1^0 \in \mathscr{F}(\mathcal{O})$ say, be such that $(\Psi, \psi_1^0\Psi_0) \neq 0$. This can always be arranged, since Ψ_0 is a cyclic vector. Let $\{g_\tau\}$, $a \leq \tau \leq b$, say, be a one-parameter group of automorphisms satisfying 1 and 2; it is not necessary to assume 3, though this will hold in the cases of interest like isotopic spin transformations. We shall therefore assume 3, to make the discussion clearer.

Let $\mathcal{O}_T$ denote the double cone in Minkowski space, whose backbone is a line of length 2T through the origin in the time direction; that is, $\mathcal{O}_T$ is the set of points $\{x; |x_0| < T \text{ and } |\vec{x}| < |T - x_0|\}$. Suppose that corresponding to each $\mathcal{O}_T$ we may choose the $U_T(\tau)$ of axiom 2 such that

1. $U_T(\tau)$ is strongly continuous in τ, with Ψ_0 and Ψ in the domain of the generator ρ_T;
2. $\|\rho_T\Psi\|$ and $\|\rho_T\Psi_0\|$ are bounded by polynomials in T.

Suppose that the group $\{g_\tau\}$ transforms operators with the quantum numbers of ψ_1 into operators with the quantum numbers of ψ_2, like an isotopic spin transformation. Then for ψ_1^0 chosen earlier we have

$$(\Psi, [\rho_T, \psi_2^0]\Psi_0) = (\Psi, \psi_1^0\Psi_0) \text{ for some } \psi_2^0 \in \mathcal{F}(\mathcal{O})$$

for all T sufficiently large.

The previous discussion is more concerned with establishing the notation and making the theorem precise than in justifying the assumptions physically. Later we shall show that the hypotheses are natural ones in any Wightman theory.

Under the above conditions we have the following theorem.

Theorem 2. The automorphism $\psi \to \psi_\tau$ of $\mathcal{F}$ does not commute with the time translations.

Proof: We assume the converse of the theorem and arrive at a contradiction.

Define $\psi_2^0(t) = U(t)\psi_2^0U(-t)$, where U(t) is time displacement. Similarly we define $\psi_1(t)$. Since g_τ commutes with time translations, we have, for large T, $G_T(t) = (\Psi, [\rho_T, \psi_2(t)]\Psi_0) = (\Psi, \psi_1(t)\Psi_0) \equiv F(t)$, say for some interval of t, which covers the line as $T \to \infty$.

We can give a meaning to integrals of the form $\int \psi(t)f(t)\,dt$ for any $f \in \mathcal{S}(\mathbb{R}_1)$ as a weak integral, since U(a) is continuous and therefore weakly measurable.

Let $f_0 \in \mathcal{S}(\mathbb{R}_1)$ have energy spectrum in a small neighborhood of Δ, and choose f_0 such that $F(f_0) = \int F(t)f_0(t)\,dt$ is nonzero. That this can always be done is shown as follows: If $\tilde{f}_0(E)$ has support near the region Δ, then $\psi_1(f_0)$ is an operator changing the energy of a state by vectors near Δ. Thus the value of $(\Psi, \psi_1(f_0)\Psi_0)$ depends only on the values of $\tilde{f}_0$ in Δ. Thus, if $(\Psi, \psi_1(f_0)\Psi_0) = 0$ for all f_0 with spectrum in the neighborhood of Δ, it vanishes for all test functions, and therefore $F(t) = 0$ as a distribution in t. But these matrix elements are entire functions of t since Ψ has bounded energy, and so we would conclude $F(0) = 0$, a contradiction. Therefore we may choose $f_0 \in \mathcal{S}$ with the desired property. Let us now choose a series of functions $\{f_T\}$ such that

a. $f_T \to f_0$ in $\mathcal{S}$ as $T \to \infty$
b. $\int \psi_2(t) f_T(t)\, dt \in \mathscr{F}(\mathscr{O}_T)$ for $T \geq T_0$, say
c. $f_T(t) = f_0(t)$ if $-T/2 \leq t \leq T/2$
d. $f_T(t) \in \mathscr{D}[-3T/4, 3T/4] \subset \mathscr{D}[-T, T]$
e. $|f_T(t)| \leq |f_0(t)|$ if $-T \leq t \leq T$.

This can always be done. The proof, except for b, is an elementary exercise in test function theory. To prove b, we note that $\psi_2 \in \mathscr{F}(\mathscr{O})$ for some $\mathscr{O}$, and so $\psi_2(t) \in \mathscr{F}(\mathscr{O}_t)$; for t such that $-3T/4 \leq t \leq 3T/4$, all the $\psi_2(t)$ will lie in some $\mathscr{F}(\mathscr{O}_T)$ if T is chosen large enough, so that $\mathscr{O} \subset \mathscr{O}_{T/4}$. Then the weak integral $\int f_T(t)\psi_2(t)\, dt$ lies in $\mathscr{F}(\mathscr{O}_T)$, since we assume the local rings weakly closed. This proves b. Then we have

$$G_T(f_T) = F(f_T) \to F(f_0) \neq 0 \quad \text{as } T \to \infty.$$

We now remark that $\psi_2(f_0)\Psi_0 = 0$ since this state has energy in the neighborhood of Δ, and this is lower than m_2, the threshold for $\mathscr{H}_2$. Also, $\psi_2(f_0)^*\Psi = 0$, since $\psi_2(f_0)^*$ destroys exactly the amount of energy that makes $\psi_2(f_0)^*\Psi$ a state with energy in the neighborhood of $m_0/2$ smaller than any state with the quantum numbers of $\psi_2^*\psi_1$. It follows that $G_T(f_T) = (\Psi, [\rho_T, \psi_2(f_T - f_0)]\Psi_0)$ for all T. Now let $T \to \infty$. The left-hand side converges to $F(f_0) \neq 0$, and the right-hand side is bounded by

$$|(\Psi, \rho_T \psi_2(f_T - f_0)\Psi_0)| + |(\Psi, \psi_2(f_T - f_0)\rho_T \Psi_0)|$$

$$\leq (\|\rho_T \Psi\| \, \|\psi_2 \Psi_0\| + \|\rho_T \Psi_0\| \, \|\psi_2 \Psi\|) \left\{ \int \max_{t \geq \frac{T}{2}} |(1 + t^2)(f_T(t) - f_0(t))| \frac{dt}{1 + t^2} \right\}$$

$$\leq (\|\rho_T \Psi\| \, \|\psi_2 \Psi_0\| + \|\rho_T \Psi_0\| \, \|\psi_2 \Psi\|)\, 2\pi \max_{t \geq \frac{T}{2}} |(1 + t^2) f_0(t)|$$

Since $f_0(t) \in \mathcal{S}$, $\max_{t \geq T/2} |f_0(t)| \to 0$ faster than any power of $1/T$, and therefore

$$(\Psi, [\rho_T, \psi_2(f_T - f_0)]\Psi_0) \to 0 \text{ as } T \to \infty,$$

contradicting $F(f_0) \neq 0$. This completes the proof.

5. Connection with Wightman Theory

We are concerned with a Wightman theory of fields $\phi_0(x) \cdots$ and a conserved current $j^\mu(x)$ in the Borchers class [4] of these fields. We want to show how one can use $j^\mu(x)$ to define the operators ρ_T having the properties of Theorem 2. Let us examine the hypotheses made in order to prove Theorem 2.

It does not seem possible to prove Goldstone's theorem for a discrete symmetry; so far, a strongly continuous group has been necessary in all proofs.

Given a conserved current $j^\mu(x)$, it is likely to have no meaning (as a distribution in x) when restricted to a sharp time. This seems to be the case for all Wick powers of the free field, for example. As mentioned before [29; 31], this can be overcome by smearing in time. We now give the argument in full, since it is nowhere published.

Let $\mathcal{O}_T$ be a double cone as already defined, and let $\theta(\vec{x})$ be a test function $\in \mathscr{D}(\mathbb{R}^3)$ which is equal to 1 on the sphere $\|\vec{x}\| \leq 2T$; and let $\alpha(t)$ be a test function $\in \mathscr{D}(\mathbb{R}_1)$ which is such that $\int \alpha(t)\, dt =$ and $\alpha(t) = 0$ for $|t| > T/2$, say. Then for all functions θ and α with this property we can prove the next theorem.

<u>Theorem 3.</u> Let $\rho_T = \int \alpha(t)\theta(\vec{x}) j^0(x,t) d^3x\, dt$. Then for any field $\phi(y)$ in the Borchers class, the expression

$$\phi'(y) = [\rho_T, \phi(y)]$$

is independent of α and θ if $y \in \mathcal{O}_T$.

<u>Proof:</u> The usual axioms imply that

$$\left[\int j^0(\underline{x},t)\theta(\underline{x}) d^3x, \phi(y)\right] = X(t,y)$$

is a continuous map from $\mathscr{D}(\mathbb{R}^1 \times \mathbb{R}^4)$ into unbounded operators, the latter set furnished with the weak topology supplied by vectors in the domain D of Wightman. It follows that we may form

$$\frac{\partial}{\partial t} X(t,y) = \left[\int \frac{\partial j^0}{\partial t}(\vec{x},t)\theta(\vec{x})\, d^3x, \phi(y)\right]$$

$$= \left[\int \left(\frac{\partial j^1}{\partial x_1} + \frac{\partial j^2}{\partial x_2} + \frac{\partial j^3}{\partial x_3}\right)\theta(\vec{x})\, d^3x, \phi(y)\right]$$

$$= -\left[\int \left(j^1(\vec{x},t)\frac{\partial\theta(\vec{x})}{\partial x_1} + j^2(\vec{x},t)\frac{\partial\theta(\vec{x})}{\partial x_2} + j^3(\vec{x},t)\frac{\partial\theta(\vec{x})}{\partial x_3}\right) d^3x, \phi(y\right.$$

Now $\partial\theta(\vec{x})/\partial x_j$ is a smooth test function with support spacelike relative to y provided $\theta = 1$ on a set whose causal shadow contains the point y.

Therefore $\partial X(t, y)/\partial t = 0$ as a distribution, and so $\int \alpha(t) X(t, y)\, dt$ is independent of α provided $\int \alpha(t)\, dt = 1$ and α is zero at those times t when y is not in the causal shadow of the set $\mathcal{O}$ at time t, which is the case here. Q. E. D.

In order to define a unitary operator for each $\mathcal{O}_T$ as $U_T(t) = e^{i\rho_T t}$ such that the action of $U_T(t)$ on the field $\phi(x)$ is independent of θ and α, we need to assume that the smeared current $j^\mu(f)$ has a unique self-adjoint extension that also commutes with the field for spacelike separation. It is not known whether this is the case for the Wick polynomials, and it may not be true in general. However, if our sole problem is to prove the Goldstone theorem as in Theorem 2, the self-adjointness of ρ_T is not important.

It is clear that the action of ρ_T on the field is independent of small time translations, that is, $[U(t_0)\rho_T U(-t_0), \phi(x)]$ is independent of t_0 for small t_0, since this merely changes $\alpha(t)$ into $\alpha(t - t_0)$. That Ψ and Ψ_0 are in the domain of ρ_T follows from the much stronger domain conditions already assumed in the Wightman theory. The polynomial boundedness condition on $\|\rho_T \Psi_0\|$ and $\|\rho_T \Psi\|$ can be easily proved if we assume that $j^\mu(x)$ is a tempered distribution. The latter assumption is usually made, and is implicit in the proof outlined before [30], since we take the Fourier transform of $j^0(x)$ and assume it is a distribution in the Schwartz sense.

This argument shows that the hypotheses of Theorem 2 are reasonable.

6. Physical Consequences

We can apply Theorem 2 to prove that the proton-neutron mass difference is not caused by a symmetry breakdown of the spontaneous type, as defined in this paper. This holds even if the sharp mass spectrum of the proton is dissolved by a cloud of photons (this means, the proton cannot be represented by an irreducible representation of the Poincaré group). For, the lowest state with the quantum numbers of the neutron is the proton + electron + soft neutrino, and this is separated by a finite gap (the electron mass) from the proton mass. Thus, to apply the theorem, we need only choose Ψ to be a state containing the proton and a cloud of very soft photons.

It should be mentioned that there is a certain type of theory that is completely outside our formulation; in such a theory it is possible to have a spontaneous breakdown of symmetry without the occurrence of the unwanted zero-energy states, at least, as physical states. This is the class of theories with a "gauge field." A theory of this type may be formulated in a manifestly covariant and causal way only by introducing an indefinite metric into the space of states (those with negative "norm," of course, do not represent physical states). There is no physical difficulty with such theories; they can always be formulated in the usual Hilbert space, and the set of observables satisfy the requirements of Haag and Araki, (as far as can be seen heuristically). In the latter formulation, however, the spinor fields lose their manifest covariance, and so the Lorentz covariance of the theory requires elaborate verification. Moreover, the manifest causality of the theory breaks down, in the sense that, in the formulation without indefinite metric, the spinor fields do not commute with the observables at spacelike separation. This does not violate actual causality, since the spinor fields are not observable. It does mean, however, that if we formulate a symmetry in terms of transformations of such fields, then we cannot prove Goldstone's theorem, since spacelike commutativity was used in the proof. The work of Borchers shows that in a "gauge" theory one can always define other operators carrying the correct quantum numbers which do commute at spacelike separation with the observables. In this paper we have formulated the symmetry as a transformation of these manifestly causal operators. Someone wishing to avoid Theorem 2 could still do so by using a formulation without manifest causality. If one works with an indefinite metric and manifest causality, then the zero-energy states of Goldstone exist, but might have negative norm; that is, they might be unphysical. Thus it is a matter of taste how one formulates a symmetry in quantum field theory, and this has led to much discussion on the validity of the proof of Goldstone's theorem. We have seen here that a rigorous proof can be given, that is applicable if one formulates a symmetry in terms of the field algebra $\mathscr{F}$, as is done here.

The two hypotheses, (1) that the thresholds of the states in $\mathscr{H}_1$ and $\mathscr{H}_2$ are different, and (2) that there are no "zero-energy" states with quantum numbers of $\psi_1^*\psi_2$, are related physically and mathematically. Physically, if there were states of low mass, with the quantum numbers of $\psi_1^*\psi_2$, then the ψ_2 would decay into ψ_1 + these states, and so the threshold of states with the quantum numbers of $\mathscr{H}_2$ would be m_1 and not m_2. Thus hypothesis 2 implies hypothesis 1. Mathematically, using techniques of analytic completion, one can prove that hypothesis 2 implies hypothesis 1 within the Wightman framework [28] provided one may rule out the accidental vanishing of certain matrix elements.

Theorem 2 does not rule out the possibility that the μ - e mass difference is due to a spontaneously broken symmetry, because of the existence of states with two neutrinos of arbitrarily small energy. However, the mass difference in that case would be due to the intervention of neutrinos, and would be related (see [30]) to the inverse lifetime of the μ, a very small number. It is a completely unknown question whether the mass differences in a spontaneously broken symmetry can be large compared to the forces in the mechanism of the breakdown.

At the conference Haag announced a generalization of Theorem 2. Kastler, Swieca, and Robinson show that no spontaneous breakdown of a continuous symmetry group is possible without "zero-energy" states (even if the mass thresholds m_1 and m_2 are equal).

References

1. Araki, H., J. Math. Phys., 1, 492 (1960).
2. Araki, H., J. Math. Phys., 4, 1343 (1963) and 5, 1 (1964).
3. Araki, H., Local Quantum Theory, book to be published by W. A. Benjamin, New York.
4. Borchers, H. J., Nuovo Cimento, 15, 784 (1960). See also Reference 32, p. 168.
5. Borchers, H. J., Commun. Math. Phys., 1, 57 (1965).
6. Borchers, H. J., Commun. Math. Phys., 1, 281 (1965).
7. Coester, F., and R. Haag, Phys. Rev., 117, 1138 (1960).
8. Doplicher, S., Commun. Math. Phys., 1, 1 (1965).
9. Goldstone, J., A. Salam, and S. Weinberg, Phys. Rev., 127, 965 (1962).
10. Guénin, M., and G. Velo, "On Symmetry Groups and Automorphisms of the Observables," to appear.
11. Guralnik, G. S., Phys. Rev., 136, B1404, B1417 (1964).
12. Guralnik, G. S., "Gauge Invariance and the Goldstone Theorem," in Proceedings of Seminar on Unified Field Theories of Elementary Particles, H. Rechtenberg, ed., Max Planck Institute, 1965.
13. Guralnik, G. S., C. R. Hagen, and T. W. B. Kibble, Phys. Rev. Letters, 13, 585 (1964).
14. Haag, R., Kgl. Danske Videnskab. Selskab, Mat.-Fys. Medd., 29, No. 12 (1955). See also Reference 32, p. 161.
15. Haag, R., Colloques sur les Problèmes Mathématiques de la Théorie Quantique des Champs, Centre National de Recherches Scientifiques, Paris, 1959.
16. Haag, R., Nuovo Cimento, 25, 287 (1962).
17. Haag, R., and D. Kastler, J. Math. Phys., 5, 848 (1964).
18. Haag, R., and B. Schröer, J. Math. Phys., 3, 248 (1962).
19. Hall, D., and A. S. Wightman, Kgl. Danske Videnskab. Selskab, Mat.-Fys. Medd., 31, No. 5 (1957). See also Reference 32, p. 161.

20. Jost, R., in Lectures on Field Theory and the Many-Body Problem, E. R. Caianiello, ed., Academic Press, New York, 1961. See also Reference 32, p. 163.

21. Kibble, T. W. B., J. Math. Phys., 6, 1022 (1965).

22. Lange, R., Phys. Rev. Letters, 14, 1, 3 (1965).

23. Lipkin, D. M., J. Math. Phys., 5, 696 (1964).

24. Misra, B., Helv. Phys. Acta, 38, 189 (1965).

25. Misra, B., Personal communication.

26. Segal, I. E., Mathematical Problems of Relativistic Physics, American Mathematical Society, Providence, R. I., 1963.

27. Segal, I. E., Illinois J. Math., 6, 500 (1962).

28. Streater, R. F., J. Math. Phys., 1, 231 (1960).

29. Streater, R. F., J. Math. Phys., 5, 581 (1964).

30. Streater, R. F., Phys. Rev. Letters, 15, 475 (1965).

31. Streater, R. F., "Spontaneous Breakdown of Symmetry in Axiomatic Theory," Proc. Roy. Soc. (London), 287A, 510 (1965).

32. Streater, R. F., and A. S. Wightman, PCT, Spin and Statistics, and All That, W. A. Benjamin, New York, 1964.

33. Wightman, A. S., Phys. Rev., 101, 860 (1956). See also Reference 32, p. 117.

Chapter 10

A METHOD FOR EUCLIDEAN QUANTUM FIELD THEORY

K. Symanzik

1. Introduction

At the conference two years ago I discussed Euclidean quantum field theory (EQFT) in general, its definition, and some of its properties [13], so I will be brief.

For simplicity, consider first the axiomatic theory of a Hermitian scalar field $A(x)$ in d dimensions (realistically, $d = 4$). The Wightman functions $\langle A(x_1) \cdots A(x_n)\rangle$ possess analytic continuations in the vector variables $\zeta_i = x_i - x_{i+1}$ $(i = 1 \cdots n-1)$. In particular the Schwinger points [12] $\mathrm{Re}\,\zeta_i^0 = 0$, $\mathrm{Im}\,\zeta_i^k = 0$ $(k = 1 \cdots d-1)$ lie [11] in the interior of the permuted extended tube, provided no two arguments (with change of notation) $x_i = (x_i^1 \cdots x_i^{d-1} x_i^d)$, $x_i^d = ix_i^0$ $(i = 1 \cdots n)$ coincide. The Wightman functions at these points we call Schwinger functions, $S(x_1 \cdots x_n)$. They are symmetric, invariant under the Euclidean (proper inhomogeneous orthogonal) group, and real if the theory is invariant under either space reflection or time reversal (P resp. T is valid).

For the axiomatic theory of one non-Hermitian scalar field we obtain from $\langle B(x_1) \cdots B(x_m)B^+(y_1) \cdots B^+(y_n)\rangle$, in an analogous manner, the functions $S(x_1 \cdots x_m, y_1 \cdots y_n)$. They are symmetric in the x and y variables separately, and go under exchange of the x and y into their complex conjugates if P is valid, or into themselves if the theory is invariant under charge conjugation. The functions are real if T or CP is valid. If there exists the usual charge operator (generator of gauge transformations of the first kind) and the vacuum is an eigenstate of it, then $S(x_1 \cdots x_m, y_1 \cdots y_n) = 0$ unless $m = n$.

If certain plausible assumptions [13, 15] concerning limiting processes on functions represented by functional integrals are made, the Schwinger functions are the "equal-time" vacuum expectation values to certain Hamiltonian theories (in d space dimensions and one time dimension) of the type studied by Araki [1].

The cluster property as well as a positive-definiteness property of Schwinger functions [15] therefore have their natural interpretation.

The positive-definiteness condition for Wightman functions is not used in the introduction of Schwinger functions. Therefore, quantum electrodynamics (QED), in, for example, the Landau gauge, is admissable, as are also theories [13, 15] with Pais-Uhlenbeck regularization [9].

2. Kirkwood-Salsburg and Mayer-Montroll Integral Equations

The theory of one non-Hermitian scalar field described by the Lagrangian density

$$L = \partial^{\mu}B^{+}\partial_{\mu}B - m^2B^{+}B - \frac{1}{2}g(B^{+}B)^2 + \alpha B^{+}B, \tag{1}$$

with α a suitable constant, satisfies the Wightman axioms in (renormalized) perturbation theory provided $d \leq 3$. The unrenormalized perturbation theoretical expansions for the Schwinger functions may be written [14]

$$S(x_1 \cdots x_m, y_1 \cdots y_n) = 0 \text{ unless } m = n, \tag{2}$$

$$S(x_1 \cdots x_n, y_1 \cdots y_n) = \sum_{\pi \in \gamma_n} S(x_1 y_{\pi(1)}, \ldots, x_n y_{\pi(n)}), \tag{3a}$$

$$S(x_1y_1, \ldots, x_ny_n) = \prod_{i=1}^{n} \left[\frac{1}{2}\int_0^{\infty} ds_i \exp\left(-\frac{1}{2}m^2 s_i\right) \int P^{s_i}_{x_i y_i}(dw_i)\right] \times n(w_1 \cdots w_n). \tag{3b}$$

Here $P^s_{xy}(dw)$ is the conditional Wiener measure[2] on continuous paths $x(\sigma)$ of time length s, with $x(0) = y$ and $x(s) = x$, and normalized such that

$$\int P^s_{xy}(dw) = (2\pi s)^{-\frac{1}{2}d} \exp\left[-\frac{1}{2}s^{-1}(x-y)^2\right].$$

The term $n(w_1 \cdots w_n)$ is a functional of n paths w_i of lengths s_i and satisfies the EQFT analogue of the classical Kirkwood-Salsburg (KS) equation [7]

[2]We use the notation of Reference 5, Appendix, except for choosing a unit particle mass.

$$n(w_1 \cdots w_n) = \exp\left(-\frac{1}{2}V_{11} - \sum_{i=2}^{n} V_{1i}\right) \sum_{\ell=0}^{\infty} (-1)^{\ell}(\ell!)^{-1}$$

$$\times \prod_{j=1}^{\ell}\left[\int_0^{\infty} t_j^{-1}\, dt_j \exp\left(-\frac{1}{2}m^2 t_j\right)\int dz_j \int P_{z_j z_j}^{t_j}(d\overline{w}_j)K(w_1, \overline{w}_j)\right]$$

$$\times\ n(w_2 \cdots w_n w_1 \cdots w_{\ell}). \tag{4}$$

Here $n(\phi) = 1$, empty products are one, and (written more generally, for use in Equation 6)

$$V_{ii} = -\alpha s_i + \frac{1}{4} g \int_0^{s_i} d\sigma_i \int_0^{s_i} d\sigma_i'\, \delta[x_i(\sigma_i) - x_i(\sigma_i')], \tag{5a}$$

$$V_{ii'} = \frac{1}{4} g \int_0^{s_i} d\sigma_i \int_0^{t_{i'}} d\sigma_{i'}\, \delta[x_i(\sigma_i) - x_{i'}(\sigma_{i'})], \qquad (i \neq i'), \tag{5b}$$

and

$$K(w_i, \overline{w}_j) = 1 - \exp(-V_{i\bar{j}}), \tag{5c}$$

where

$$V_{i\bar{j}} = \frac{1}{4} g \int_0^{s_i} d\sigma_i \int_0^{t_j} d\tau_j\, \delta[x_i(\sigma_i) - z_j(\tau_j)]. \tag{5d}$$

Iterating Equation 4 n - 1 times gives the analogue of the Mayer-Montroll (MM) equation [7]

$$n(w_1 \cdots w\ ) = \exp\left(-\frac{1}{2}\sum_{i=1}^{n} V_{ii} - \sum_{i<i'} V_{ii'}\right)\sum_{\ell=0}^{\infty} (-1)^{\ell}(\ell!)^{-1}$$

$$\times \prod_{j=1}^{\ell}\left[\int_0^{\infty} t_j^{-1}\, dt_j \exp\left(-\frac{1}{2}m^2 t_j\right) \int dz_j \int P_{z_j z_j}^{t_j}(d\overline{w}_j)K(w_1 \cdots w_n, \overline{w}_j)\right]$$

$$\times\ n(\overline{w}_1 \cdots \overline{w}_{\ell}), \tag{6}$$

where

$$K(w_1 \cdots w_n, \overline{w}_j) = 1 - \exp\left(-\sum_{i=1}^{n} V_{i\bar{j}}\right). \tag{5e}$$

Equation 6 shows that (at least if renormalization does not destroy this property, see Section 4) $n(w_1 \cdots w_n)$ depends only on the occupation time distributions

$$b(v, w_i) = \int_0^{s_i} d\sigma_i\ \delta(v - x_i(\sigma_i)) \equiv b_i(v),$$

called, for brevity, "blobs." Introducing for functionals F(b) of a blob the integral over blobs

$$\int Q(db)F(b) \equiv \int_0^{\infty} s^{-1}\, ds\, \exp\left(-\frac{1}{2} m^2 s\right) \int dx \int P^s_{xx}(dw)F(b(\cdot\,, w))$$

and abbreviating

$$n(w_1 \cdots w_n) = \hat{n}(b_1 \cdots b_n) \equiv n(1 \cdots n),$$

we may write Equation 4

$$n(1 \cdots n) = \exp\left(-\frac{1}{2} V_{11} - \sum_{i=2}^{n} V_{1i}\right) \sum_{\ell=0}^{\infty} (-1)^{\ell} (\ell!)^{-1} \times \prod_{j=1}^{\ell}\left[\int Q(d\overline{b}_j)K(1, \overline{j})\right] n(2 \cdots n\overline{1} \cdots \overline{\ell}), \tag{7}$$

where now

$$V_{11} = -\alpha \int dv\, b_1(v) + \frac{1}{4} g \int dv\, b_1(v)^2,$$

$$V_{1i} = \frac{1}{4} g \int dv\, b_1(v) b_i(v),$$

and

$$K(1,\bar{j}) = \exp(-V_{1\bar{j}})$$

and similarly for Equation 6.

The classical KS equation for distribution functions in the grand canonical ensemble of particles interacting by a pair potential $V(x - x')$ is[3]

$$n(x_1 \cdots x_n) = \exp\left[\beta\mu - \beta \sum_{i=2}^{n} V(x_1 - x_i)\right] \sum_{\ell=0}^{\infty} (-1)^{\ell}(\ell!)^{-1}$$

$$\times \prod_{j=1}^{\ell}\left(\int dz_j \left\{1 - \exp\left[-\beta V(x_1 - z_j)\right]\right\}\right) n(x_2 \cdots x_n z_1 \cdots z_{\ell}) \tag{8}$$

with $n(\phi) = 1$, empty products being one, $\beta = (kT)^{-1}$, and μ the chemical potential. Thus, the (classically only translational) degree of freedom in Equation 7 is a blob, the interblob interaction is determined by the overlap of blobs, and the chemical potential is replaced by a blob self-interaction. This suggests that we apply to Equations 4 and 6 methods that have been successful in classical (CSM) [10] and Quantum (QSM) [5, 6] statistical mechanics.

3. Methods of Solution and Regularization

Equations 4, 6, and 8 may be written

$$N = N_0 + \mathrm{Op}N, \tag{9}$$

where N is the vector $(n(1), n(12), \cdots)$, N_0 is the contribution to the right-hand sides from $n(\phi) = 1$, and Op is, respectively, a Wiener or blob, or (in Equation 8) ordinary integral operator. If the norm of Op is smaller than one in a suitable Banach space that contains N_0, then Equation 9 has a unique solution that can be obtained by iteration. In CSM this is satisfied [10] for a large class of potentials if for given temperature the activity is sufficiently small. The convergent series solutions of Equation 8 so obtained are the fugacity expansions of the distribution functions. Similar results were obtained in QSM for a slightly more restricted class of potentials [6].

The fugacity expansions converge at most for the gas phase, however. For condensed phases other methods of solving Equa-

[3]See, for example, J. Lebowitz and J. K. Percus [7].

tion 8 must be attempted. The usual procedure is to approximate in Equation 9 by breaking the vector N off in some way (for example, by neglecting clusters beyond a certain size), and to solve the resulting closed system of equations numerically, a procedure reminiscent of (so far much less successful) approximations in quantum field theory.

For Equations 4 and 6 the following results [14] are obtained:

d = 0: This is a mathematical model only and exactly solvable. The KS equation 4 has only one, the correct, solution (while the corresponding usual Green's functions equations have three linearly independent solutions), that for $\alpha < m^2$ can be obtained by iteration, and for $\alpha > m^2$ only if g is not too large. The same holds for the MM equation 6, except that if the iteration solution does not converge there may be more than one solution for particular values of α and g.

d = 1: This is the (two-dimensional) anharmonic oscillator for imaginary time. Equations 4 and 6 can be solved by iteration provided

$$\text{Re } g > 0, \qquad \text{Re}(m^2 - \alpha) > 3\left(\frac{|g|}{4}\right)^{2/3}$$

and give functions analytic in α and g in this domain.

d = 2 and d = 3: Equations 4 and 6 have only the trivial solution $n(w_1 \cdots w_n) = 0$ almost everywhere (a.e.) unless $\alpha = \infty$. This must be handled by renormalization. However, if one regularizes Equations 4 and 6 by cutting off the t-integrations at the lower (and for convenience only, also upper) limit and by using in Equations 5a, b, and d regularized delta-functions, then the iteration solutions of Equations 4 and 6 converge with finite α for any number of dimensions if g is not too large.

4. Renormalization

Equations 4 and 6 lead immediately, as they stand for $d \geq 2$, to divergences, since, for example, the double integral in Equation 5a, the square integral of the occupation time distribution of a conditional Brownian motion, is a.e. infinite on Wiener space. In perturbation theory, the correct choice for α is

$$\alpha = 2gG(0) + \delta m^2, \tag{10}$$

where

$$G(x - y) = (2\pi)^{-d} \int dK\, (K^2 + m^2)^{-1} \exp[iK(x - y)], \tag{11}$$

which is $(4\pi|x - y|)^{-1} \exp(-m|x - y|)$ for $d = 3$, and δm^2 is a negative constant (logarithmically infinite for $d = 3$). See Equation 23.

Inspection of Equations 4 and 6 and comparison with perturbation theory show the following way to isolate the divergencies (described here only for Equation 6). Introduce reduced functionals by

$$n_r(1 \cdots n) = n(1 \cdots n) - \sum_{i=1}^{n} f(b_i) n(1 \cdots \not{i} \cdots n) + \sum_{i<i'} f(b_i) f(b_{i'}) \times n(1 \cdots \not{i} \cdots \not{i}' \cdots n) - + \cdots$$

where arguments crossed out are omitted. The simplest suitable choice for f(b) is

$$f(b) = \exp\left[-\frac{1}{2} V_{bb} - \int Q(d\bar{b}) K(b, \bar{b})\right] \equiv 1 + \varepsilon(b), \tag{12}$$

whereupon with $\rho(1 \cdots n) = n_r(1 \cdots n) f(b_1)^{-1} \cdots f(b_n)^{-1}$ Equation 6 becomes

$$\rho(1 \cdots n) = \sigma(1 \cdots n) - \sum_{i=1}^{n} \sigma(1 \cdots \not{i} \cdots n) + \sum_{i<i'} \sigma(1 \cdots \not{i} \cdots \not{i}' \cdots n) - + \cdots \tag{13a}$$

with

$$\sigma(1 \cdots n) = \exp\left\{-\sum_{i<i'} V_{ii'} + \int Q(db)\left[\varepsilon(b) K(b_1 \cdots b_n, b) - \sum_{i=1}^{n} K(b_i, b) + K(b_1 \cdots b_n, b)\right]\right\} \sum_{\ell=0}^{\infty} (-1)^{\ell} (\ell!)^{-1} \times \prod_{j=1}^{\ell}\left[\int Q(d\bar{b}_j) K(b_1 \cdots b_n, \bar{b}_j) f(\bar{b}_j)\right] \rho(\bar{1} \cdots \bar{\ell}) \tag{13b}$$

and

$$\rho(\phi) = \sigma(\phi) = 1.$$

Written more explicitly, Equation 12 is

$$f(w) = \exp\left[\frac{1}{2}\alpha s - \frac{1}{8} g \int_0^s d\sigma \int_0^s d\sigma' \, \delta[x(\sigma) - x(\sigma')]\right.$$

$$- \int_0^\infty dt\, t^{-1} \int dz \int P^t_{zz}(d\overline{w}) \left(1 - \exp\left\{- \frac{1}{4} g \int_0^s d\sigma\right.\right.$$

$$\left.\left.\left.\int_0^t d\tau\, \delta[x(\sigma) - z(\tau)]\right\}\right)\right] \tag{14}$$

which has to be made finite to the extent that the problem posed by Equation 13 is meaningful. This also requires that $\varepsilon(w)$ be "sufficiently small," namely, roughly of order s as $s \to 0$.

The expression in braces in Equation 14 may be written

$$1 - e^{-L} = L - \frac{1}{2}L^2 + \frac{1}{2}L^3 \int_0^1 d\lambda (1 - \lambda)^2 \, e^{-\lambda L}. \tag{15}$$

The last term lies between 0 and $L^3/6$, which, for $d \leq 3$, is integrable to an a.e. finite functional of sufficient smallness, as shown with use of the later formula 26b upon an easy calculation. The first term, L, is canceled in Equation 14 by a part gG(0) of α. The second term, $-L^2/2$, upon use of Equation 26b, gives for d = 3

$$- \frac{g^2}{128\pi^2} \int_0^s d\sigma \int_0^s d\sigma' \frac{\exp\left[-2m\left|x(\sigma) - x(\sigma')\right|\right]}{[x(\sigma) - x(\sigma')]^2}, \tag{16}$$

which is a.e. negative infinite, but not as strongly as the remaining integral in Equation 14, which we therefore treat first. The following method is adapted from Nelson [8].

Let

$$A(x) = \int dK \, e^{iKx} \widetilde{A}(K).$$

Then

$$\int_0^s d\sigma \int_0^s d\sigma' A(x(\sigma) - x(\sigma')) = \int dK \, \widetilde{A}(K) \left| \int_0^s d\sigma \, e^{iKx(\sigma)} \right|^2. \tag{17}$$

We note that the conditional Brownian motion from y to x in time s is given by

$$x(\sigma) = s^{-1}[\sigma x + (s - \sigma)y] + (s - \sigma) \int_0^{\sigma} dx_w(\sigma')(s - \sigma')^{-1},$$

where $x_w(\sigma)$ is ordinary Brownian motion, and is thus a Gaussian Markov process to which the Itô formula

$$dW[x(\sigma)] = dx_\alpha(\sigma + 0)\partial_\alpha W[x(\sigma)] + \frac{1}{2} \Delta W[x(\sigma)]\, d\sigma$$

applies. (In this formula the summation convention is used and $dx(\sigma + 0)$ is the increment of the position vector during a time interval $d\sigma$ following the time σ.) Setting $W(x) = e^{iKx}(K^2)^{-1}$ and restricting ourselves for simplicity to closed trajectories, we may rewrite Equation 17 as

$$\int_0^s d\sigma \int_0^s d\sigma' \, A[x(\sigma) - x(\sigma')]$$

$$= \int_0^s dx_\alpha(\sigma) \int_0^{s\wedge} dx_\beta(\sigma') B_{\alpha\beta}[x(\sigma) - x(\sigma')] + sB_{\alpha\alpha}(0) \tag{18a}$$

with

$$B_{\alpha\beta}(x - x') = \left(\frac{\partial^2}{\partial x_\alpha \partial x'_\beta}\right) B(x - x') \tag{18b}$$

and

$$B(x - x') = 4 \int dK (K^2)^{-2} \exp[iK(x - x')]\, \widetilde{A}(K). \tag{18c}$$

The $\wedge$-integral in Equation 18a is the multiple stochastic integral as defined by Nelson, which (in view of Equation 21 and the formulas preceding) we will abbreviate as $:XBX: = XBX - \mathrm{Tr}B$, the double dots denoting here and more generally later the omission of coincidence terms. For fixed $x(\cdot)$, B is an integral operator on the space $[0, s] \otimes (1, \cdots, d)$, while X symbolizes the vector $dx_\alpha(\sigma + 0)$, with integrations and summations being suppressed in the notation. For the last term in Equation 18a, $A(x) = \frac{1}{4} g\delta(x)$ gives

$$sB_{\alpha\alpha}(0) = \frac{sg}{(2\pi)^d}\int \frac{dK}{K^2}$$

$$= sgG(0) + \frac{sgm^2}{(2\pi)^d}\int \frac{dK}{K^2(K^2+m^2)} \qquad (19)$$

whereof the first term must be canceled by gG(0) in α, while the second term is finite. (For d = 2 this term is infrared divergent. This spurious divergence can be prevented by slightly rewriting the Itô formula in such a way that in Equation 18c $(K^2 + m^2)^{-2}$ replaces $(K^2)^{-2}$, and in Equation 18a two more terms appear.)

We have arrived, for d = 3, at the expression $\exp(-\frac{1}{2} : XBX :)$ with

$$B_{\alpha\beta}(x - x') = (8\pi)^{-1}g\,|x - x'|^{-3}[\delta_{\alpha\beta}(x - x')^2 - (x_\alpha - x'_\alpha)(x_\beta - x'_\beta)], \qquad (20)$$

which is positive semidefinite. While the stochastic integral itself is sufficiently well behaved, its exponential is not. We can amend this as follows: Using [8]

$$dx_\alpha(\sigma)\,dx_\beta(\sigma') = :dx_\alpha(\sigma)\,dx_\beta(\sigma'): + \delta_{\alpha\beta}\delta(\sigma - \sigma')\,d\sigma\,d\sigma'$$

or, more generally,

$$\exp\left[\int_0^s dx_\alpha(\sigma)\,f_\alpha(\sigma)\right]$$

$$= :\exp\left[\int_0^s dx_\alpha(\sigma)\,f_\alpha(\sigma)\right]: \exp\left[\frac{1}{2}\int_0^s d\sigma\,f(\sigma)^2\right],$$

one easily derives

$$\exp\left(-\frac{1}{2} : XBX :\right)$$

$$= :\exp\left[-\frac{1}{2}XB(1+B)^{-1}X\right]: \exp\left[-\frac{1}{2}\mathrm{Tr}\ln(1+B) + \frac{1}{2}\mathrm{Tr}\right. \qquad (21)$$

Since B is positive semidefinite, $(1 + B)^{-1}$ and $\ln(1 + B)$ exist. The last exponent contains the divergent term

$$\frac{1}{4}\mathrm{Tr}B^2 = \frac{g^2}{128\pi^2}\int_0^s d\sigma \int_0^s d\sigma' \,|x(\sigma) - x(\sigma')|^{-2}.$$

Combining this with Equation 16, we obtain

$$\frac{g^2}{64\pi^2}\int_0^s d\sigma \int_0^s d\sigma' \,\frac{\exp\left[-m|x(\sigma) - x(\sigma')|\right]}{(x(\sigma) - x(\sigma'))^2}$$
$$+ \frac{g^2}{128\pi^2}\int_0^s d\sigma \int_0^s d\sigma' \left(\frac{1 - \exp\left[-m|x(\sigma) - x(\sigma')|\right]}{|x(\sigma) - x(\sigma')|}\right)^2, \qquad (22)$$

whereof the second term is bounded for finite s while the first may again be transformed according to Equations 18. From

$$\hat{A}(x) = -\frac{g^2}{32\pi^2}\frac{e^{-m|x|}}{x^2} = -\frac{g^2}{32\pi^2}\int dK \,\frac{e^{iKx}}{2\pi^2|K|}\arctan\frac{|K|}{m}$$

we find (accounting also for the last term in Equation 19)

$$\delta m^2 = -\frac{g^2}{16\pi^4}\int dK \,\frac{\arctan\frac{|K|}{m}}{|K|^3} + \frac{gm^2}{8\pi^3}\int \frac{dK}{K^2(K^2 + m^2)} \qquad (23)$$

and

$$\hat{B}_{\alpha\beta}(x - x') = \left(\frac{\partial^2}{\partial x_\alpha \partial x'_\beta}\right)\hat{B}(x - x'), \qquad (24a)$$

where

$$\hat{B}(x - x') = -\frac{g^2}{16\pi^4}\int dK \,\frac{\exp\left[iK(x - x')\right]}{|K|^5}\arctan\frac{|K|}{m}. \qquad (24b)$$

We may still rewrite the product

$$:\exp\left[-\frac{1}{2}XB(1 + B)^{-1}X\right]:\exp\left(-\frac{1}{2}:X\hat{B}X:\right),$$

for which one easily finds

$$: \exp\left[-\frac{1}{2}X(B+\hat{B})(1+B+\hat{B})^{-1}X\right]:$$

$$\exp\left[\frac{1}{2}\,\mathrm{Tr}\,\ln(1+B)+\frac{1}{2}\,\mathrm{Tr}\,\hat{B}-\frac{1}{2}\,\mathrm{Tr}\,\ln(1+B+\hat{B})\right].$$

Collecting all terms, we have

$$f(w) = :\exp\left[-\frac{1}{2}X(B+\hat{B})(1+B+\hat{B})^{-1}X\right]: \exp(C_1+C_2+C_3), \quad (25)$$

where

$$C_1 = -\int_0^{\infty} t^{-1}\,dt \int dz \int P^t_{zz}(d\overline{w})\,\frac{1}{2}L^3 \int_0^1 d\lambda(1-\lambda)^2\,e^{-\lambda L}$$

with

$$L = \frac{1}{4}g\int_0^s d\sigma \int_0^t d\tau\;\delta[x(\sigma)-z(\tau)].$$

The second term in Equation 22 is C_2, and

$$C_3 = -\frac{1}{2}\,\mathrm{Tr}\,\ln(1+B+\hat{B})+\frac{1}{2}\,\mathrm{Tr}(B+\hat{B})-\frac{1}{4}\,\mathrm{Tr}\,B^2$$

$$= \frac{1}{2}\int_0^1 d\lambda(1-\lambda)\,\mathrm{Tr}\left[(B+\hat{B})^2(1+\lambda B+\lambda\hat{B})^{-2}-B^2\right].$$

From Equations 20 and 24 in Fourier form one easily sees that $B + \hat{B}$ is positive semidefinite provided $0 \leq g \leq 2\pi m$, but no significance should be attached to this bound since the representation in Equation 25 is not unique (see, for example, the remark after Equation 19), and especially since the effect of Equation 25 in Equation 13 unknown.

It can, however, be checked that insertion of Equation 25 in Equation 13 no longer leads to divergencies, at least if all terms generated in the iteration solution of Equation 13 (starting from $\rho(\emptyset) = 1$, $\rho(1) = \rho(12) = \cdots = 0$) are expanded in powers of g. The proof is lengthy, but straightforward with use of

$$\int_0^\infty ds\, e^{-\frac{1}{2}m^2 s} \int P_{xy}^t(dw) : \int_0^s d\sigma_1 \int_0^{\sigma_1} d\sigma_2 \cdots \int_0^{\sigma_{n-1}} d\sigma_n$$

$$\times \prod_{i=1}^{n} \delta(x_i - x(\sigma_i)) \prod_{i\in I} \dot{x}(\sigma_i + 0) :$$

$$= 2^{n+1} \prod_{i=1}^{n} [G(x_{i-1} - x_i)(\overleftarrow{\partial}_{x_i})^{\alpha_i}]\, G(x_n - y), \tag{26a}$$

with $x_0 \equiv x$, $\dot{x}(\sigma_i + 0)\, d\sigma_i \equiv dx(\sigma_i + 0)$, and $\alpha_i = \{1 \text{ if } i \in I,\ 0 \text{ otherwise}\}$, and

$$\int_0^\infty t^{-1}\, dt\, e^{-\frac{1}{2}m^2 t} \int dz \int P_{zz}^t(d\overline{w}) : \int_0^t d\tau_1 \cdots \int_0^t d\tau_n$$

$$\times \prod_{i=1}^{n} \delta(z_i - z(\tau_i)) \prod_{i\in I} \dot{z}(\tau_i + 0) :$$

$$= 2^n \sum_{\pi\in\gamma_{n-1}} \prod_{i=1}^{n} [G(z_{\pi(i-1)} - z_{\pi(i)})(\overleftarrow{\partial}_{z_{\pi(i)}})^{\alpha_i}], \tag{26b}$$

where $z_{\pi(0)} \equiv z_{\pi(n)} \equiv z_n$, and the sum goes over the permutations of the indices $1 \cdots n-1$. It is hereby seen that the transversality of Equation 20 is crucial for the elimination of divergent terms.

The discussion of Equation 25 and, more important still, of Equations 13 without reference to expansion in powers of g has not yet been given.

5. Conventional Regularization

If one regularizes the interaction term in the Hamiltonian corresponding to Equation 1 as

$$\frac{1}{2} \int d\vec{x} \int d\vec{x}' : B^+(\vec{x}, x^0) B(\vec{x}, x^0) : v(\vec{x} - \vec{x}') : B^+(\vec{x}', x^0) B(\vec{x}', x^0) :$$

and to define the Wick products (with "free" contraction function), performs a limiting process of mathematically still unclarified validity, one can, at the stage of reduced functionals (Equation 13), obtain expressions with $V(x - x') = v(\vec{x} - \vec{x}')\delta(x^d - x'^d)$ replacing $g\delta(x - x')$ in Equation 5, and in addition in Equation 14 $1 - e^{-L}$ replaced by $1 - L - e^{-L}$. Upon expansion, the conventionally regularized perturbation series would now be obtained. The discussion of Equation 13 in this form would be a preparatory step to the investigation of the equation, unregularized, with substitution of Equation 25.

6. Relation to QSM

Equations 4 and 6 closely resemble equations derived in QSM by Ginibre [5]. For purposes of comparison, let $\rho_\beta(x_1 \cdots x_n, y_1 \cdots y_n)$ be the reduced density matrices for the grand canonical ensemble of nonrelativistic spinless neutral Bose particles, of mass M and interacting by the pair potential

$$V_\beta(x - y) = \frac{1}{4} M^{-2}\beta\, \delta^\beta_{reg}(x - y), \tag{27}$$

with $\beta = (kT)^{-1}$, the chemical potential $\mu(\beta) = -(2M)^{-1}m^2 + \Delta\mu(\beta)$, and δ^β_{reg} a regularized delta-function such that $\delta^\beta_{reg} \to \delta$ as $\beta \to 0$ Then, upon suitable choice of $\Delta\mu(\beta)$,

$$\lim_{\beta\to 0} \left(\frac{\beta}{2M}\right)^n \rho_\beta(x_1 \cdots x_n, y_1 \cdots y_n) = S(x_1 \cdots x_n, y_1 \cdots y_n) \tag{28}$$

holds. The proof rests on comparing Equations 13 and 14 with their QSM counterparts, which differ from them essentially only be a discretization of the τ, σ, and t integrations in units β. If, however, in Equation 27 $g\delta^\beta_{reg}$ is taken as the V of the conventional regularization just discussed, the corresponding regularized Euclidean Green's functions are obtained in Equation 28. (Even then $\Delta\mu(\beta) \to \infty$ if $d > 1$. Note also that for finite β $\delta^\beta_{reg} \neq$ is necessary unless $d = 1$.)

If orthodox ideas about renormalization are correct, one should obtain also the EQFT functions for $d = 4$ by merely replacing in Equations 27 and 28 β by $\beta'(\beta)$ resp. $\beta''(\beta)$ to absorb the now necessary coupling-constant and amplitude renormalizations.

In any case, Equation 28 shows that $S(x_1 \cdots x_n, y_1 \cdots y_n)$ must be nonnegative, a conclusion reached also more generally [14] for models, as will be shown later, that are not related to QSM.

7. Other Models

If instead of Equation 1 the Lagrangian density for one Hermitia scalar field

$$L = \frac{1}{2}\partial^{\mu}A\partial_{\mu}A - \frac{1}{2}m^2A^2 - \frac{1}{8}gA^4 + \frac{1}{2}\alpha A^2$$

is chosen, Equations 2 and 3a, but not Equation 3b are changed slightly, and in Equations 4 and 6 each t-integration must be given the factor one half. This excludes relating this model to QSM, as just discussed, but is not expected to influence the question of existence of a solution.

If, however, the Lagrangian density for two scalar fields in trilinear interaction

$$L = \partial_{\mu}B^{+}\partial^{\mu}B - M^2B^{+}B + \frac{1}{2}\partial^{\mu}A\partial_{\mu}A - \frac{1}{2}m^2A^2$$

$$- gB^{+}BA + \alpha' B^{+}B + \frac{1}{2}\beta' A^2 + \gamma A \qquad (29)$$

is chosen, for the Green's functions that do not contain the A-field essentially Equations 4 and 6 are again obtained with, however, in Equation 5 $g\delta(x - x') \to -4g^2G(x - x')$. In CSM or QSM terms this means that the repulsive contact interaction has been replaced by an attractive (singular) finite-range interaction, and a result of Fisher and Ruelle [4] excludes the possibility of obtaining the corresponding EQFT by a limiting process on QSM, as described before. (This would also hold if in Equation 1 g were chosen negative instead of positive.) Thus, existence of an EQFT to Equation 29, or Equation 1 with $g < 0$, is most unlikely, a conclusion in accord with the result of Baym [2] on the corresponding Minkowski QFT.

Scalar QED requires the use of stochastic integrals already before renormalization because of derivative coupling but seems, for $d \leq 3$, not to lead to any serious complication compared to the model described by Equation 1. Spin one half QED requires use of the two-component formalism as already invisaged by Feynman [3]. Now σ-matrices carrying an ordering parameter will appear, but one may hope that they give no new difficulty to principle.

Acknowledgment

The research reported in this paper was supported in part by a grant from the Ford Foundation and in part by a grant from the National Science Foundation.

References

1. Araki, H., J. Math. Phys., 1, 492 (1960).
2. Baym, G., Phys. Rev., 117, 886 (1960).

3. Feynman, R. P., Phys. Rev., 84, 108 (1951), Appendix D.

4. Fisher, M., and D. Ruelle, J. Math. Phys., 7, 260 (1966).

5. Ginibre, J., J. Math. Phys., 6, 238 (1965).

6. Ginibre, J., J. Math. Phys., 6, 252, 1432 (1965).

7. Lebowitz, J., and J. K. Percus, J. Math. Phys., 4, 1495 (1963).

8. Nelson, E., Analysis in Function Space, eds. W. T. Martin and I. Segal, M.I.T. Press, Cambridge, Mass. (1964), p. 87.

9. Pais, A., and G. E. Uhlenbeck, Phys. Rev., 79, 145 (1950).

10. Ruelle, D., in Lectures in Theoretical Physics, University of Colorado Press, Boulder (1964), Vol. VI, p. 37; Rev. Mod. Phys., 36, 580 (1964).

11. Ruelle, D., Doctoral thesis, University of Brussels (1959); Nuovo cimento, 19, 356 (1961).

12. Schwinger, J., Proc. Natl. Acad. Sci. U.S., 44, 956 (1958).

13. Symanzik, K., in Analysis in Function Space, eds. W. T. Martin and I. Segal, M.I.T. Press, Cambridge, Mass. (1964), p. 197.

14. Symanzik, K., J. Math. Phys., 7, 510 (1966).

15. Symanzik, K., "A Modified Model of Euclidean Quantum Field Theory," IMM-NYU, 327; CIMS, New York University (June 1964).

Chapter 11

INFRAPARTICLE STRUCTURE AND FUNCTIONAL INTEGRALS

Jan Tarski

1. Introduction

The investigation which is described in this note originated in an attempt to understand some standard expressions for Green's function of quantized fields. The expressions in question are functional integral representations, in terms of the fermion Green's functions for given external fields [1, 14]. Such representations have so far only a formal meaning, since they contain the usual divergences. Our goal was to construct similar but divergence-free integrals for a few soluble models. We were partially successful, and we can easily represent some related functions, but not Green's functions themselves.

At the previous Endicott House conference, and also at this one, various other studies were presented, where functional integrals were applied to model field theories, for instance [15]. We should say that the models which are considered in this paper are much more modest, and it is not clear to what extent the present approach can be applied to more complicated interactions.

We shall give a special emphasis to infrared effects, for two reasons. First, this author has recently been interested in the description of such effects, and second, they lead to some interesting modifications of the functional integrals. For readers' convenience we will now summarize how such effects come about in simple models.

We recall that there is no free scalar massless field in two dimensions, which would fulfill the usual requirements. The standard construction of the Fourier transform of the two-point function yields a divergence,

$$\langle \varphi(x)\varphi(y)\rangle_0 \sim \frac{1}{4\pi}\int_{-\infty}^{\infty} \frac{dp^1}{|p^1|} \exp[-ip(x - y)]. \qquad (1)$$

(Here and in similar expressions, $p^0 = |p^1|$ is understood.) There are two natural ways to define modified fields [16, 19].

First, one can restrict the test functions $\tilde{f}(p)$ by the condition $\tilde{f}(0) = 0$. The resulting field φ_P yields a positive definite metric, as usual, but one cannot form Wick monomials $:\varphi_P^n:$ for $n \geq 3$, so as to obtain nonzero vacuum expectation values. Second, one can regularize the integrand in Equation 1 by making the replacement,

$$\omega^{-1}\theta(\omega) \to (d/d\omega)[\theta(\omega) \log \omega], \tag{2}$$

where $\omega = |p^1|$. The resulting field φ_K yields an indefinite metric, but one can form all monomials $:\varphi_K^n:$, and also the exponential $:\exp(ig\varphi_K):$.

With the help of the field φ_K, one can write Heisenberg fields for Schroer's model [10, 16, 19]:

$$\varphi_P(x);\ \psi(x) = \psi^{(0)}(x) : \exp(ig\varphi_K) : (x), \tag{3}$$

where $\psi^{(0)}$ is a free fermion field. The scalar field is free, and we choose φ_P rather than φ_K. We find that the application of φ_P, ψ, and $\overline{\psi}$ to the vacuum then yields a space of states with a positive definite metric. The field φ_K can also be useful for the study of several other models [19], for instance, the Thirring model. In these models one encounters fields (such as ψ in Equation 3) which exhibit an infraparticle structure: their discrete mass is dissolved into a continuum.

A similar situation arises in the four-dimensional Bloch-Nordsieck model [1, Sec. 41; 17]. There one needs, for example, the time integral of the temporal component of the free electromagnetic potential $A_0^{(0)}$. The time integral yields an additional factor $|\underset{\sim}{k}|^{-1}$ for a Fourier component, and if

$$B(x) = \int^t dt'\, A_0^{(0)}(t', \underset{\sim}{x})$$

(where the integral has to be carefully defined), then

$$\langle B(x)B(y)\rangle_0 \sim \frac{-1}{2(2\pi)^3} \int \frac{d^3k}{|k|^3} \exp[-ik(x-y)].$$

Again regularization is needed.

In the remaining sections, we shall limit ourselves to Schroer's model and to its analogue, in which φ_K and φ_P are both replaced by the field φ_μ with mass $\mu > 0$. The resulting model will be called the massive gauge model. However, our discussion applies directly to the Bloch-Nordsieck model, and also to gauge transformations in quantum electrodynamics [1, Sec. 40].

Let us now give a description of the paper. In Section 2 we present some representations which involve the Hilbert space integral. They are elementary, but it appears that they have not been stated explicitly before.

In Section 3 we try to adapt the Hilbert space integral to the case of indefinite metric associated with the field φ_K. Our construction of the integral is a preliminary one, and we emphasize several shortcomings. On the other hand, our construction is simple, and perhaps the most natural one to try. Therefore we felt justified in including a short presentation.

Finally, in Section 4 we complete an earlier analysis of the charged sectors of Schroer's model by showing that the representation of φ_P in a given sector is irreducible, and a fortiori cyclic. The representation is also myriotic (non-Fock), and we can generalize a functional integral expression of Section 2, for example, by employing perpendicular measures.

2. Some Functional Integral Representations

The following formula will be basic in our discussions. Let φ be a free scalar field, in n dimensions and of arbitrary mass. Then, for suitable functionals F_j,

$$\langle F_1\{\varphi^{(-)}\}\, F_2\{\varphi^{(+)}\}\rangle_0 = \int \mathscr{D}(\eta^-)\, \mathscr{D}(\eta^+) \exp\left[-(\eta^-, \eta^+)\right] F_1\{\eta^-\} F_2\{\eta^+\}. \tag{4}$$

The fields $\varphi^{(\pm)}(p)$ are to be normalized so that $[\varphi^{(-)}(\underset{\sim}{p}), \varphi^{(+)}(\underset{\sim}{q})] = \delta(\underset{\sim}{p} - \underset{\sim}{q})$. The integral [5, 11] is over the Hilbert space of functions satisfying $\int d^{n-1}\underset{\sim}{p}|\eta^\pm|^2 < \infty$, and $\eta^\pm$ are complex conjugates. The variance is one-half. (See Note added in proof, and also Equation 13, with $\sigma = 1$.) The notation is as in [15].

If the functionals F_j have a Volterra expansion, then each side of Equation 4 reduces to (see for instance [14])

$$F_1\{\delta/\delta\eta^+\}\, F_2\{\eta^+\}\Big|_{\eta^+=0}. \tag{5}$$

However, Equation 4 suggests the possibility of defining other functionals, for example, $|\varphi^{(+)}(f)|$, as operators in the Fock space.

For comparison we note another representation,

$$\langle F\{\varphi\}\rangle_0 = \int \mathscr{D}(\eta) \exp\left[-\tfrac{1}{2}(\eta, \eta)\right] F\{\eta\}, \tag{6}$$

which is related to Equation 4 by $\varphi = \varphi^{(-)} + \varphi^{(+)}$ and $\eta = 2^{-\frac{1}{2}}(\eta^- + \eta^+)$. If one assumes a fixed time, then the representation 6 is a corollary to theorems of Gelfand [6] and of Segal [12]. Similar representations have also been suggested by Coester and Haag [2], but on the basis of heuristic arguments.

Equation 4 can be used to analyze the difficulties with the functional integral expressions for Green's functions. We shall consider in particular the massive gauge model. The calculations are analogous to those in [1, Sec. 40], and formally one has

$$\langle(\psi(x)\bar{\psi}(y))_+\rangle_0 \sim G^{(0)}(x - y) \int \mathscr{D}(\zeta) \exp\left(iA^{(0)}\{\zeta\}\right) \exp\{ig[\zeta(x) - \zeta(y)]\}. \tag{7}$$

Here $A^{(0)}$ is the free-field action, $G^{(0)} \exp\{ig[\zeta(x) - \zeta(y)]\}$ is the Green's function for the external field ζ, and the closed loop functional does not contribute. The space of functions ζ has not been specified. A formal evaluation of the integral yields the desired function after an infinite factor is removed.

Let us compare this formal expression with the following rigorou expression for a regularized Wightman function:

$$\begin{aligned} W_{reg}(x - y) &= W^{(0)}(x - y)\langle \exp[ig\varphi_\mu^{(-)}(f_x)] \exp[-ig\varphi_\mu^{(+)}(f_y)]\rangle_0 \\ &= W^{(0)}(x - y) \int \mathscr{D}(\eta^-)\, \mathscr{D}(\eta^+) \exp[-(\eta^-, \eta^+)] \exp\{ig[\eta^-(f_x) - \eta^+(f_y \end{aligned} \tag{8}$$

$$\varphi_\mu^{(\pm)}(f_w) = \int d^2u\,\varphi_\mu^{(\pm)}(u) f(w - u). \tag{9}$$

We can determine $\eta^\pm(f_w)$ by expressing $\varphi_\mu^{(\pm)}(f_w)$ in terms of $\varphi_\mu^{(\pm)}(p^1$ We may remark that a regularization of the form $(\exp[ig\varphi_\mu^{(\pm)}])(f_w)$ would be just as good.

The differences between the integrals 7 and 8 are summarized by the following properties of Equation 8:

1. Positive and negative frequencies are separated.
2. The Bose field is regularized.
3. A Wightman function rather than a Green's function is represented.

We shall comment on these properties in turn. Regarding the first, one can see from Equation 6 that the integral 7 corresponds to the (formal) unrenormalized solution $\psi^{(0)}(x) \exp[ig\varphi_\mu(x)]$, and such a quantity has not yet been defined. Thus, property 1 relates to renormalization.

Regarding the second property, if we let $f_W \to \delta_W$, then the integral 8 will not converge as a Hilbert space integral. However, we can still say that it will converge in a distribution-theoretic sense. One needs this qualification, even though the value of the integral would be a smooth function for $x \neq y$.

A simpler example of a distribution-theoretic convergence is the following:

$$\int \mathscr{D}(\eta^-)\, \mathscr{D}(\eta^+) \exp\left[-(\eta^-, \eta^+)\right]\eta^-(p^1)\eta^+(q^1) = \delta(p^1 - q^1). \tag{10}$$

Here, as in some other instances, δ is really a distribution on $L_2 \times L_2$.

Regarding the third property, note that in Expression 7 the action $A^{(0)}$ has (in the integrand) the factor $p^2 - m^2$, which yields $(p^2 - m^2)^{-1}$ upon integration. One then gets the causal function by employing Feynman's prescription $m^2 \to m^2 - i\epsilon$. Therefore, in order to adapt the integral 8 for the causal function, it may be necessary to combine Hilbert space integration with contour integration. We shall not consider this matter further.

3. Integration Over Spaces With Indefinite Metric

Our problem now is to adapt the ideas of the previous section to Schroer's model. Of course, that section applies directly to φ_P, if the functionals are suitably restricted. We know, however, that the field φ_K rather than φ_P occurs in the solution ψ.

An obvious approach is to generalize Equation 4 to φ_K. In particular, we can try to integrate over the one-particle sector of φ_K, and to allow also such functionals F_j which require (after integration) the regularization 2. Then Equation 8 would remain valid, as a special case of Equation 4.

The regularization 2 seems to require that the test functions have, for instance, a continuous derivative. However, our plan is to modify the Hilbert space integral. For this modification it will be convenient to use an orthonormal basis and a complete space. The indefinite metric complicates the completion, but only slightly, and the details can be found in a recent note [3].

The completion yields a Π_1-space, whose metric is characterized by the signature $(-, +, +, +, \cdots)$. However, the construction that follows generalizes trivially to spaces of type Π_k, having k minuses (a finite number) in the signature of the metric. For a general theory of Π_k-spaces, see [8].

Let us select an orthonormal basis for Π_1, say $\{v_j\}_{j \geq 0}$, so that for $c \in \Pi_1$,

$$c = \sum_{j\geq 0} c^j v_j, \quad \langle c, c \rangle = -|c^0|^2 + \sum_{j\geq 1} |c^j|^2. \tag{11}$$

The space Π_1 has a natural topology, for example, the topology induced by the norm

$$\|c\|^2 = \sum_{j\geq 0} |c^j|^2. \tag{12}$$

Our definition of an integral over Π_1 depends on starting with a Hilbert space integral corresponding to the norm 12. However, we generalize by associating the variance σ with the coordinate c^0, the remaining variances being fixed at, for example, unity. We then try to continue analytically to $\sigma = -1$.

Explicitly, let F(c) be a functional on the sequence space Π_1. Let F be approximated by functionals $F_n(c^0, \cdots, c^n)$, the sequence being suitable for the convergence of the Hilbert space integral. Actually, one has $F(c^0, c^{0*}, \cdots)$ because Π_1 is complex, and we shall write $c^{j+,-}$ in place of c^j, c^{j*}, respectively. Now we set

$$I_\sigma(F) = \lim_{n\to\infty} \frac{1}{(2\pi i)^{n+1}} \frac{1}{\sigma} \int_C dc^{0+} dc^{0-} \exp(-|c^{0\pm}|^2/\sigma) \int_C dc^{1+} dc^{1-}$$

$$\exp(-|c^{1\pm}|^2) \cdots F_n(c^{0\pm}, \ldots, c^{n\pm}). \tag{13}$$

Here $dc^{j+}dc^{j-} = 2id(\mathrm{Re}\, c^{j+})d(\mathrm{Im}\, c^{j+})$, and regarding σ, see Note added in proof. Suppose that $I_\sigma(F)$, as defined by this formula, is analytic in a neighborhood of $\sigma = 1$. If $I_\sigma(F)$ can be continued analytically to a neighborhood of the interval $[-1, 1]$, then we define

$$\int_{\Pi_1} \mathscr{D}(c^-)\, \mathscr{D}(c^+) \exp(-\langle c^\pm, c^\pm\rangle)\, F(c^+, c^-) \equiv I_{-1}(F). \tag{14}$$

The exponential $\exp(-\langle c^\pm, c^\pm\rangle)$ is of course symbolic.

This definition is with respect to the chosen basis $\{v_j\}$. We may also consider an alternate basis $\{Uv_j\}$ where U is unitary, that is, 1-1 onto and such that $\langle b, c\rangle = \langle Ub, Uc\rangle$. Now, if F is integrable with respect to $\{v_j\}$, it is desirable that it have these additional properties. We say that F has

Property A if F is integrable with respect to every orthonormal system $\{Uv_j\}$,
Property B if it has Property A and if $I_{-1}(F)$ is unitary-invariant, that is, if evaluations with respect to $\{v_j\}$ and with respect to $\{Uv_j\}$ are always equal.

Let us investigate the integrability of various functionals. For brevity in writing, we now assume a real space Π_1. (Cf. Equation 17 in the following.)

Lemma 1. Let $E(c) = \exp\left(\sum_{j\geq 0} E_j c^j\right)$, where $\sum |E_j|^2 < \infty$. Then

$$I_{-1}(E) = \exp \frac{1}{2}\left(-E_0^2 + \sum_{j\geq 1} E_j^2\right), \tag{15}$$

and E has Property B.

Lemma 2. Let P(c) be a polynomial functional,

$$P(c) = P(0) + \sum P_j c^j + \cdots + \sum P_{j_1 \cdots j_n} c^{j_1} \cdots c^{j_n},$$

which is totally invariantly traceable ("invariantly" referring to the norm, Equation 12). Let $P_i(c) = P(ic^0, c^1, c^2, \cdots)$. Then P_i is also totally invariantly traceable with respect to the norm 12, also

$$I_{-1}(P) = I_1(P_i), \tag{16}$$

and P has Property B.

Proofs: The evaluations of $I_\sigma(E)$ and $I_\sigma(P)$ are elementary, and yield Equations 15 and 16. For trace requirements, see references [5; notes, Chapter VII] and [7]. Traceability of P_i, of course, follows from that of P. To establish Property A, write $U = U'U_{01}U''$, where U' and U'' do not affect the index 0, and U_{01} affects the indices 0 and 1 only. (This factorization follows as in the case of the Lorentz group, see [9].) Property B now follows from Equations 15 and 16.

It is also easy to find nonintegrable functionals, as follows:

1. If $F(c) = |c^0|$, then

$$I_\sigma(F) = (2\pi\sigma)^{-\frac{1}{2}} \int_{-\infty}^{\infty} dc^0 |c^0| \exp[-(c^0)^2/2\sigma] = (2\sigma/\pi)^{\frac{1}{2}}. \tag{17}$$

2. If $F(c) = \exp[-\frac{1}{2}(c^0)]$, then $I_\sigma(F) = (\sigma + 1)^{-\frac{1}{2}}$.

Let us conclude this section by noting a few of the features found in Section 2, which are lacking in the present integral. First, we are not sure whether or not integrability is always basis-independent. Second, the evaluations 5 and 10 do not apply directly. Third, it is not clear whether for example the operators $\exp ig\varphi_\kappa{}^{(\pm)}(f)$ yield integrable functionals (cf. [3; Section 3, second remark]).

4. Charged Sectors in Schroer's Model

One generally thinks of infrared effects as associated with a myriotic representation of a massless field. In case of Schroer's model, $Z_3 = 1$, and any vector generates a cyclic representation of φ_P.

Let us consider for example the sector of unit charge. As shown in [16; Section 4], it suffices to consider the action of φ_P on vectors of the form

$$\upsilon_f = \exp[ig\varphi_\kappa^{(+)}](f)\,|0\rangle; \tag{18}$$

that is, the free fermion factors can be ignored, and pairs $:\exp(ig\varphi_\kappa): \; :\exp(-ig\varphi_\kappa):$ can be expressed in terms of φ_P. Moreover, if ζ is future timelike, then the vector

$$\upsilon_{x+i\zeta} = \exp[ig\varphi_\kappa^{(+)}(x + i\zeta)]\,|0\rangle \tag{19}$$

yields a cyclic representation which is irreducible. The representation space will be denoted by $\mathscr{H}_{x+i\zeta}$. Now, if we set

$$q^{\pm}(p^1) = \mp ig \exp(\mp ipx - p\zeta)\,(4\pi|p^1|)^{-\frac{1}{2}}, \tag{20}$$

$$A^{(\pm)}(p^1) = \varphi_P^{(\pm)}(p^1) - q^{\pm}(p^1), \tag{21}$$

then $A^{(-)}(p^1)\upsilon_{x+i\zeta} = 0$ for all p^1, and this specifies the representation of the canonical commutation relations.

We now assert, that the space $\mathscr{H}_{x+i\zeta}$ in fact is the entire sector of unit charge, aside from the free-fermion states. One has to show that $\upsilon_f \in \mathscr{H}_{x+i\zeta}$ for normalizable states υ_f, and we sketch a proof of this fact.

Consider the operators

$$P^\mu = \int_{-\infty}^{\infty} dp^1 p^\mu \varphi_P^{(+)}(p^1)\varphi_P^{(-)}(p^1) \tag{22}$$

It is consistent to write φ_P, since P^μ leaves the charge sectors invariant, and we verify this for the following special case:

$$\exp(-iPw)\upsilon_{x+i\zeta} = \exp\left(\int_{-\infty}^{\infty} dp^1 (\exp(-ipw) - 1)\,\varphi_P^{(+)}(p^1) q^-(p^1)\right)\upsilon_{x+i\zeta}. \tag{23}$$

Equation 23 can be obtained by reducing to normal form as in [1, Sec. 39]. Note that the Fock property of $A^{(\pm)}$ allows us to replace $A^{(-)}$ by $\delta/\delta A^{(+)}$. The coefficient of $\varphi_P^{(+)} = A^{(+)} + q^+$ and analogy with the Fock case show that the exponential acts on $\upsilon_{x+i\zeta}$ as a unitary operator. (An exponential of $A^{(-)}$ acts trivially on $\upsilon_{x+i\zeta}$, and can be supplied.) We conclude $\exp(-iPw)\upsilon_{x+i\zeta} \in \mathscr{H}_{x+i\zeta}$.

We now observe that

$$\exp[-iP(y - x)]\,\upsilon_{x+i\zeta} = \upsilon_{y+i\zeta}. \tag{24}$$

Such vectors (for a fixed ζ) are dense in the space of vectors of form υ_f. Therefore $\upsilon_f \in \mathscr{H}_{x+i\zeta}$, as asserted.

It may be of interest to note that, while the denseness of vectors $\upsilon_{x+i\zeta}$ can be easily demonstrated, directly, it is also a consequence of the Tauberian theorem for an L_2-space [18].

Let us now enlarge the space of one-particle states of φ_P, so as to allow a countably additive measure. Then we can generalize Equation 4 for the sector of charge Q, by choosing a cyclic vector v_Q and a measure $d\mu_Q$ such that

$$\langle v_Q, F_1\{\varphi_P^{(-)}\}F_2\{\varphi_P^{(+)}\}v_Q\rangle = \int d\mu_Q(\eta^-, \eta^+)F_1\{\eta^-\}F_2\{\eta^+\}. \tag{25}$$

The unit charge, the integral is determined by the values of F_j on functions $\eta^\pm$ such that

$$\int_{-\infty}^{\infty} dp^1 |\eta^\pm - q^\pm|^2 < \infty; \tag{26}$$

for sectors of different charge, the measures are perpendicular (cf. [4]). Alternately, one can utilize inequivalent probability distributions, as in [13].

Equation 25 resembles the assertion of Gelfand's theorem. However, this theorem as stated in [6] is not interesting for Schroer's model, since the singularities cancel when one forms $\varphi_P^{(-)} + \varphi_P^{(+)}$.

Acknowledgment

I am very grateful to Professor K. Symanzik for his patient replies to numerous questions, and for his interest in this work. I would like to thank Professor J. Feldman for a helpful discussion during the Conference.

This work was supported by a Ford Foundation grant at the Courant Institute, New York University, and by the U.S. Atomic Energy Commission at Columbia University. I would like to express my appreciation for the hospitality which I received at these institutions.

References

1. Bogolubov, N. N., and D. V. Shirkov, Introduction to the Theory of Quantized Fields, Interscience Publishers, Inc., New York, 1959, Chapter VII.

2. Coester, F., and R. Haag, Phys. Rev., 117, 1137 (1960).

3. Dubin, D. A., and J. Tarski, J. Math. Phys., 7, 574 (1966).

4. Feldman, J., Pacific J. Math., 8, 699 (1958).

5. Friedrichs, K. O., and H. N. Shapiro, Proc. Nat. Acad. Sci. U.S., 43, 336 (1951); also K. O. Friedrichs, H. N. Shapiro, et al., Integration of Functionals, lecture notes, Courant Institute, New York University, 1957.

6. Gelfand, I. M., and N. Ya. Vilenkin, Generalized Functions, Academic Press, New York, 1964, Volume 4, Chapter IV, Section 5.4, especially Theorem 5.

7. Gross, L., Trans. Amer. Math. Soc., 105, 372 (1962).

8. Iohvidov, I. S., and M. G. Krein, Trudy Moscov Mat. Obsc. 5, 367 (1956) and 8, 413 (1959); translation: Amer. Math. Soc. Transl., Ser. 2, 13, 105 and 34, 283.

9. Naimark, M. A., Uspekhi Mat. Nauk, 9, No. 4 (62), 19 (195 Section 2; trans., Amer. Math. Soc. Transl., Series 2, 379.

10. Schroer, B., Fortschritte der Physik, 11, No. 1 (1963), Section 3.

11. Segal, I. E., Ann. Math., 57, 401 (1953).

12. Segal, I. E., Trans. Amer. Math. Soc., 81, 106 (1956).

13. Segal, I. E., Trans. Amer. Math. Soc., 88, 12 (1958).

14. Symanzik, K., Z. Naturforsch., 9A, 809 (1954).

15. Symanzik, K., in Analysis in Function Space, W. T. Martin and I. Segal, eds., M.I.T. Press, Cambridge, Mass., 1964, p. 197; also in New York University report, IMM-NYU 327 (1964).

16. Tarski, J., J. Math. Phys., 5, 1713 (1964).

17. Tarski, J., J. Math. Phys., 7, 560 (1966).

18. Wiener, N., The Fourier Integral and Certain of its Applications, Dover Publications, Inc., New York, reprint from 1933, Section 15.

19. Wightman, A. S., in Proceedings of the Cargese Summer School, 1964, ed. M. Lévy, Gordon & Breach, New York, 1966.

Note added in proof. In the text we did not give an adequate explanation of the variances associated with the functional integrals. In Equation 13, σ is the mean value of $|c^{0\pm}|^2$ and is twice the usual variance. Thus, $\sigma = 1$ means variance one-half, and this is the natural choice in Equation 4. For instance, this equation and the evaluation (Expression 5) then take particularly simple forms.

Similarly, in Equation 6 the natural variance is unity. One then has an analogous evaluation

$$F\left\{\eta^+ + \frac{\delta}{\delta\eta^+}\right\}\Bigg|_{\eta^+=0} \tag{27}$$

The foregoing variances differ by a factor of 2, and this factor was also noted in a similar context in [12].

Chapter 12

ON THE STRUCTURE OF THE FINITE PARTS IN RENORMALIZABLE QUANTUM FIELD THEORIES

A. Visconti

To the memory of Yves Le Gaillard

I want to report on some work done in collaboration with J. Soffer and the late Y. Le Gaillard [9].

We have been investigating the structure of the finite parts of the propagators of a renormalizable field theory. In order to be specific, let us consider a self-interacting scalar field whose particles have the mass m_{ob} (we shall use $\kappa_{ob} = m_{ob}^2$ rather than m_{ob}). A second parameter g_{ob} will be the leading parameter in the expansions we are going to consider; it will be referred as the coupling constant. We want to discuss the structure of the vacuum expectation values of time-ordered products of N field operators $\Phi(x_j)$

$$\Delta'(x_1 \cdots x_N, g_{ob}, \kappa_{ob}) \tag{1}$$

in two different frames:

1. The type of interaction remains unspecified.
2. One considers a definite type of interaction.

1. The Type of Interaction Is Unspecified

We suppose that by means of Feynman's rules we have been able to write down explicitly the set

$$\Delta^{(s)}(x_1 \cdots x_N, \kappa_{ob}), \qquad s = 0, 1, 2, \cdots, \tag{2}$$

of the radiative corrections of the full propagator $\Delta'(x_1 \cdots x_N, g_{ob}, \kappa_{ob})$, and we form the series

$$\sum_s \frac{g_{ob}^s}{s!} \Delta^{(s)}(x_1 \cdots x_N, \kappa_{ob}). \tag{3}$$

As a matter of fact, since the $\Delta^{(s)}$ are, in all cases of physical interest, meaningless integrals of well-defined analytical functions, we are then faced with the two questions: What is the meaning of the $\Delta^{(s)}$, and once the answer to that question is obtained, what is the meaning of the series 3?

The answer to the first question is given by the method of regularization of divergent integrals: We suppose thus that the field theory we are studying is regularizable. We may then observe that the Fourier transforms of the $\Delta^{(s)}$ are given as meaningless integrals of well-defined rational functions of momenta, and we locate the interval of integration whose contribution gives a divergent result as the one including all higher values of momenta; that is, we consider the so-called ultraviolet divergences. The problem of extracting convergent parts from such integrals is an old problem in mathematics. The theory of "finite parts" devised by Hadamard has been imbedded by L. Schwartz [6] in his distributions theory and is universally known as the "theory of pseudofunctions." One proceeds in two steps.

First, instead of the meaningless integral

$$F = \int f(x)\, dx \tag{4}$$

of a well-defined function f(x), we consider another one

$$F_\lambda = \int \phi(x, \lambda)\, dx, \tag{5}$$

depending on certain parameters (corresponding to the "masses" in the Pauli-Villars method) [4] symbolized by λ. The integrand of F_λ is chosen such that the integral is convergent and for a certain value λ_0 of λ, $\phi(x, \lambda_0) \equiv f(x)$. This first step will be referred to as the "regularization" of the integral F.

Second, we try to determine a certain function of λ, $\mathscr{D}F(\lambda)$, which will be called "the divergent part of F" such that

$$\lim_{\lambda=\lambda_0} \{F(\lambda) - \mathscr{D}F(\lambda)\} = \mathscr{P}F, \tag{6}$$

$\mathscr{P}F$ being a well-defined number; this second step may be considered as the "renormalization" of the integral. Without any additional requirements (such as the ones imposed by physics), both steps (except for coherence conditions) are completely arbitrary.

The same line of reasoning may be held in quantum field theory. Replace each meaningless integral $\Delta^{(s)}$ by its regularized $\Delta_\lambda^{(s)}$, where λ represents, for instance, the auxiliary masses in the Pauli-Villars method. Now $\Delta_\lambda^{(s)}$ is a temperate distribution and satisfies $\Delta_{\lambda_0}^{(s)} = \Delta^{(s)}$, this last identity being interpreted with caution along the lines in the first step which we have just outlined. It is furthermore clear that to a given $\Delta^{(s)}$ correspond different $\Delta_\lambda^{(s)}$; we assume that there is a type of regularization compatible with the process of renormalization as it will be defined in what follows.

Coming back now to the series 3, we replace each of its terms $(g_{ob}^s/s!)\Delta^{(s)}$ by the temperate distribution $(g_{ob}^s/s!)\Delta_\lambda^{(s)}$. We are still faced with the problem of the meaning of this new series since this series is, as it happens, indeed, in all cases of physical interest, a divergent one. We shall then consider

$$\Delta_\lambda'(x_1 \cdots x_N, g_{ob}, \kappa_{ob}) = \sum_s \frac{g_{ob}^s}{s!} \Delta_\lambda^{(s)}(x_1 \cdots x_N, \kappa_{ob}) \tag{7}$$

as a formal series in g_{ob}, in this way leaving unsolved the problem of convergence of the perturbative series in quantum field theory.[1]

We now turn our attention to the renormalization step and try to find physical assumptions that will help us in defining the divergent part $\mathscr{D}\Delta_\lambda^{(s)}$ of the s-radiative correction of the propagator Δ' such that

$$\lim_{\lambda=\lambda_0} \{\Delta_\lambda^{(s)} - \mathscr{D}\Delta_\lambda^{(s)}\} = \mathscr{P}\Delta^{(s)}, \tag{8}$$

with $\mathscr{P}\Delta^{(s)}$ a temperate distribution. Let us introduce the renormalization constants as three formal series in g_{ob}.

$$Z_\lambda(g_{ob}, \kappa_{ob}), \qquad G_\lambda(g_{ob}, \kappa_{ob}), \qquad \delta\kappa(g_{ob}, \kappa_{ob}), \tag{9}$$

the first (constant) term of Z_λ being 1, and the series G_λ and $\delta\kappa_\lambda$ having no constant term. We also introduce the formal series

$$\Delta_Z(x_1 \cdots x_N, g_{ob}, \kappa_{ob}) \equiv Z_\lambda^{-N/2} \Delta'(x_1 \cdots x_N, G_\lambda, \kappa_{ob} - \delta\kappa). \tag{10}$$

---

[1]Formal series have been introduced in "Renormalization Theory" by A. S. Wightman [10].

In other words, we multiply the formal series Δ' by the $-N/2$ power of the formal series Z_λ after having performed in Δ' the following substitutions:

$$g_{ob} \to G_\lambda \qquad \kappa_{ob} \to \kappa_{ob} - \delta\kappa_\lambda. \tag{11}$$

We finally denote by $\Delta_Z^{(s)}$ the coefficients of the formal expansion of Equation 10:

$$\Delta_Z(x_1 \cdots x_N, g_{ob}, \kappa_{ob}) = \sum \frac{g_{ob}^s}{s!} \Delta_Z^{(s)} (x_1 \cdots x_N, \kappa_{ob}) \tag{12}$$

Our main renormalizability assumption can then be formulated as follows: There is a possible choice of Z_λ, G_λ, $\delta\kappa_\lambda$ such that when λ takes its critical value λ_0, all the coefficients $\Delta_Z^{(s)}$ of the series 10 become temperate distributions, $\mathscr{P}\Delta^{(s)}$ [3].

Application of the rules of calculation with formal series allows us to express the coefficients $\Delta_Z^{(s)}$ in Equation 12 as follows:[2]

$$\Delta_Z^{(m)}(x_1 \cdots x_N, \kappa_{ob}) = \sum_{s,q=0}^{s+q\leq m} C_{s,q}^{N,m} (\lambda, \kappa_{ob}) \frac{\partial^q}{\partial \kappa_{ob}^q} \Delta_\lambda^{(s)}(x_1 \cdots x_N, \kappa_{ob}) \tag{13}$$

given the following definition of the structure coefficients $C_{s,q}^{N,m}$ [6

$$Z_\lambda^{-N/2} \frac{G_\lambda^s}{s!} \frac{(-\delta\kappa)^q}{q!} = \sum \frac{g_{ob}^m}{m!} C_{s,q}^{N,m} (\lambda, \kappa_{ob}). \tag{14}$$

We may now remark that from Equation 14, with $C_{m,o}^{N,m} = 1$, formula 13 may be brought to the form

$$\Delta_Z^{(m)}(x_1 \cdots x_N, \kappa_{ob}) = \sum_{s=0}^{m-1} \sum_{q=0}^{m-s} C_{s,q}^{N,m} \frac{\partial^q}{\partial \kappa_{ob}^q} \Delta_\lambda^{(s)}(x_1 \cdots x_N, \kappa_{ob}) + \Delta_\lambda^{(m)}(x_1 \cdots x_N, \kappa_{ob}). \tag{15}$$

[2]A more careful handling is needed if one wants to be rigorous; the interested reader should see Reference 9.

We now choose Z_λ, G_λ, $\delta\kappa_\lambda$ in agreement with our renormalization assumption. Then, the theory being renormalizable, $\Delta_Z^{(m)}$ reduces to the temperate distribution $\mathscr{P}\Delta^{(m)}$, and finally the divergent part $\mathscr{D}\Delta^{(m)}$ defined as $\Delta^{(m)} - \mathscr{P}\Delta^{(m)}$ takes the following form:

$$\mathscr{D}\Delta^{(m)}(x_1 \cdots x_N, \kappa_{ob}) = -\sum_{s=0}^{m-1}\sum_{q=0}^{m-s} C_{s,q}^{N,m} \frac{\partial^q}{\partial \kappa_{ob}} \Delta^{(s)}(x_1 \cdots x_N, \kappa_{ob}), \tag{16}$$

and is expressed by means of the structure coefficients in terms of the derivatives with respect to κ_{ob} of the $\Delta^{(s)}$, which are given by Feynman's rules applied to the unrenormalized theory. One may also note that the maximum order of the derivatives is m, and that the superscript s, which denotes the order of the radiative correction, takes its values between 0 and m - 1.

In spite of their generality, the former considerations have been applied to the case of the two-point propagator of a self-interacting scalar field.[3] Using Dyson's equation, we studied the structure of its proper self-energy part, and at each order of the perturbative expansion we have been led to a system of three equations: Two of them determine the structure coefficients, while the third represents a compatibility condition that brings severe restrictions on the structure of the divergent parts concerned. Consider, for instance, any scalar self-interacting renormalizable field theory and the second radiative correction $\Pi_2^*(p^2, \kappa_{ob})$ of its self-energy part: it is a straightforward consequence of Equation 16 that in an expansion of the form

$$\Pi_2^*(p^2, \kappa_{ob}) = \Pi_2^*(-\kappa_{ob}, \kappa_{ob}) + (p^2 + \kappa_{ob}) \left.\frac{\partial \Pi^*}{\partial p^2}\right]_{p^2=-\kappa_{ob}} + \Pi_2^{*(f)}(p^2, \kappa_{ob})$$

$\Pi_2^{*(f)}$ should be a temperate distribution. Although the expressions for higher radiative corrections of Π^* tend to be more and more complicated, the former formula gives the well-known result about the unrenormalizability of interactions $g_{ob}(\Phi(x))^a$ with $a \geq 5$. Other applications have been made to the conventional and to a somewhat generalized Lee model. The interested reader should refer to Reference 9b.

2. The Type of Interaction Is Specified

In order to obtain more explicit results, one has to introduce explicitly the type of interaction. For simplicity's sake, we shall

[3] See Reference 9b.

consider again a scalar self-interacting field with an interaction of the type $g_{ob}(\Phi(x))^3$. Since, as it will appear later, the functional formulation of quantum field theory allows a straightforward approach to the renormalization problems, we want first of all to recall some of its properties [1]. Consider a free scalar field describing particles of mass $m_{ob}(\kappa_{ob} = m_{ob}^2)$ and the Lorentz invariant functional of the square integrable function J(x) (scalar with respect to Lorentz transformations):

$$u_0[J|\kappa_{ob}] = \exp\left\{-\frac{1}{4}\int J(x)\Delta(x-x')J(x')\right\}$$

$$=\sum\left(-\frac{1}{4}\right)^n\frac{1}{n!}\left(\int J(x)\Delta(x-x')J(x')\right)^n$$

$$=\sum\left(-\frac{1}{4}\right)^n\frac{1}{n!}\int J(x_1)\cdots J(x_n)\Delta(x_1-x_1')$$

$$\cdots\Delta(x_n-x_n')J(x_1')\cdots J(x_n'), \tag{17}$$

where the causal function Δ is a solution of

$$(\Box - \kappa_{ob})\Delta(x) = 2i\delta(x), \tag{18}$$

with the known boundary properties. The functional $u_0[J/\kappa_{ob}]$ is the generating functional of the vacuum expectation values of field operators. More precisely,

$$\langle 0|\phi(x_1)\cdots\phi(x_n)|0\rangle = \lim_{J\equiv 0} D_{x_1}\cdots D_{x_n}u_0[J|\kappa_{ob}], \tag{19}$$

where D_x means the functional derivative at the point x (noted also $\delta/\delta J(x)$). In what follows, we shall not need its topological definition [2] but only an algebraic one. Consider any Fréchet-Volterra type of functional:

$$A[J] = \sum_x \frac{1}{s!}\int A(x_1\cdots x_s)J(x_1)\cdots J(x_s). \tag{20}$$

Without loss of generality, the kernel $A(x_1\cdots x_s)$ (temperate distribution) can be supposed to be symmetrical with respect to all its arguments. We define

$$D_{x_1} \cdots D_{x_r} \int f(x_1 \cdots x_s) J(x_1) \cdots J(x_s) = \begin{cases} \dfrac{s!}{(s-r)!} \displaystyle\int f(x_1 \cdots x_r x_{r+1} \cdots x_s) \\ \qquad J(x_{r+1}) \cdots J(x_s) \\ \\ 0 \text{ if } r > s \end{cases} \tag{21}$$

The former definition shows that

$$\left[D_{x_j}, D_{x_k}\right] = 0, \tag{22}$$

and we assume that the functional differentiation is distributive with respect to the addition.

If we now denote by $u[J|g_{ob}, \kappa_{ob}]$ the generating functional for an interacting field, we may prove that the $\mathscr{S}$ operator is given by the following formula:[4]

$$\mathscr{S} = \lim_{J(x)\equiv 0} : \exp\left\{ - \int \phi_{in}(x) \{\Box_x - \kappa_{ob}\} D_x \right\} : \frac{1}{\mathscr{N}(g_{ob}, \kappa_{ob})} u[J|g_{ob}, \kappa_{ob}], \tag{23}$$

where $\mathscr{N}(g_{ob}, \kappa_{ob})$ is a normalizing factor for $u[J]$, that is, where

$$\mathscr{N}(g_{ob}, \kappa_{ob}) = u[J(x) \equiv 0 | g_{ob}, \kappa_{ob}]. \tag{24}$$

On the other hand, we may prove, from general principles, that the generating functional u can, for a theory with direct coupling, be obtained by applying an integrodifferential operator which depends on the type of interaction and thus represents the dynamical factor in the expression of u to the generating functional of the in-field. One has, namely,[5]

$$u[J|g_{ob}, \kappa_{ob}] = \exp\{ig_{ob}\mathscr{A}[D_\xi]\} u_0[J|\kappa_{ob}], \tag{25}$$

where $\mathscr{A}[D]$ is obtained from the interaction term

---

[4] See, for instance, Reference 1f.

[5] See, for instance, References 1d and 1f.

$$\int (\phi(\xi))^3 \, d^4\xi \tag{26}$$

when one replaces $\phi(x)$ by $(1/i)\ \delta/[\delta J(\xi)]$.

As a matter of fact, it is easy to see by a straightforward computation that the kth functional derivative of the generating functional, when J(x) has been set equal to 0, is expressed by the sam Feynman's diagrams that are associated by the conventional quantum field theory with the expressions of the radiative corrections of $\Delta'(x_1 \cdots x_k)$.

But, in order to make all our calculations less cumbersome, we need to go a step further by introducing in all our formulas the Fourier transform of the source J(x), since it is well known that the expression of a given graph is simplest when one uses a momentum representation [8]. In order to do so, we define

$$J(x) = (2\pi)^{-4} \int e^{ipx}\, j(p), \tag{27}$$

and denote

$$A[J] = A\left[(2\pi)^{-4} \int e^{ipx}\, j(p)\right] \equiv A_F[j]. \tag{28}$$

Then, one can easily prove the following formula:

$$D_x A[J] = \int d^4p \; e^{-ipx}\, D_p A_F[j]. \tag{29}$$

By a straightforward application of Equation 29, one obtains the expression of $u_F[j|g_{ob}, \kappa_{ob}]$:

$$u_F[j|g_{ob}, \kappa_{ob}] = \exp\left[-(2\pi)^{-12}\, g_{ob} \int \delta(q + q' + q'')D_q D_{q'} D_{q''}\right] u_{0F}[j|\kappa_{ob}], \tag{30}$$

with

$$u_{0F}[j|\kappa_{ob}] = \exp\left[\frac{1}{2} \int j(p)\delta(p + p')\Delta(p)j(p')\right], \tag{31}$$

and

$$\Delta(p) = (2\pi)^{-4} \frac{1}{p^2 + \kappa_{ob} - io}. \tag{32}$$

Since from now on we are going to work only in momentum space, we shall drop the suffix (F), replace $(2\pi)^{-12} g_{ob}$ by g_{ob}, and define

$$D_{qq'} \equiv D_q D_{q'}, \qquad D_{qq'q''} \equiv D_q D_{q'} D_{q''}. \tag{33}$$

We shall therefore express $u_F[j/g_{ob}, \kappa_{ob}]$ as follows:

$$u[j|g_{ob}, \kappa_{ob}] = \exp\{ig_{ob}\mathscr{A}[D]\}\, u_0[j|\kappa_{ob}], \tag{34}$$

$$i\mathscr{A}[D] \equiv -\int \delta(q + q' + q'')D_{qq'q''}. \tag{35}$$

After these preliminaries, let us return to our renormalization problem and consider

$$u_Z[j|g_{ob}, \kappa_{ob}] = \frac{1}{\mathscr{N}(g_{ob}, \kappa_{ob})} u[Z^{-\frac{1}{2}} j|G, \kappa_{ob} - \delta\kappa], \tag{36}$$

where Z, G, and $\delta\kappa$ are formal series as in Equation 9, and $\mathscr{N}$ is a normalization factor. It is clear that kth functional derivative of u_Z can be deduced from the kth derivative of u as given by Equation 33 by performing in this last quantity all the renormalization transformations which were introduced in the first part of this work. In other words, the consideration of u_Z instead of u gives globally the renormalizations transformations which, in Section 1, were performed in each propagator $\Delta'(x_1 \cdots x_k)$. The main renormalization postulate tells us, then, that there exists a special choice of the renormalization constants Z, G, $\delta\kappa$, and $\mathscr{N}$ such that[6]

$$u_Z[j|g_{ob}, \kappa_{ob}] = \mathscr{P} u[j|g_{ob}, \kappa_{ob}], \tag{37}$$

---

[6] Besides the changes in the interaction introduced by the renormalization constants, we have not considered explicit changes of this former quantity. Such a change, expressed by the counterterm $\lambda\Phi^4$, occurs when one renormalizes pseudoscalar mesons interacting with nucleons, the coupling being pseudoscalar.

where $\mathscr{P}u[\cdots]$ is a Fréchet-Volterra functional. Once again, one may be thorough and rigorous by the introduction of all the apparatus of formal series.[7]

Let us then try to compute

$$\frac{d\,\mathscr{P}u[j|g_{ob}, \kappa_{ob}]}{dg_{ob}}, \tag{38}$$

relations 36 and 37 show that $\mathscr{P}u[\cdots]$ is a function of g_{ob} through the functions $\mathscr{N}$, Z, G, $\delta\kappa$, and it is a matter of simple, but somewhat lengthy, calculations, to show that[8]

$$\frac{d\,\mathscr{P}u[j|g_{ob}, \kappa_{ob}]}{dg_{ob}} = \left\{ N + A \int j(q) D_q + B \int \delta(q + q') D_{qq'} + Ci\mathscr{A}[D] \right\} \mathscr{P}u[j|g_{ob}, \kappa_{ob}], \tag{39}$$

where the coefficients N, A, B, and C, functions of g_{ob} and κ_{ob}, are related to the renormalization constants by the following expressions:

$$N = -(\partial/\partial g_{ob}\mathscr{N})/\mathscr{N}, \qquad A = -\tfrac{1}{2}(\partial/\partial g_{ob} Z)/Z$$

$$B = -\frac{Z}{2}\,\partial\delta\kappa/\partial g_{ob}, \qquad C = Z^{3/2}\partial G/\partial g_{ob}. \tag{40}$$

---

[7]See Reference 9c.

[8]Several remarks should be made at this point. First of all, all integrals should be regularized; it is known that the $g\Phi^3$ theory is indeed regularizable. Then one has again to take advantage of the introduction of formal series if one wants to be rigorous. On the other hand, the integrodifferential operator $\mathscr{A}[D]$ introduces meaningless expressions like $\Delta(0)$. These expressions can be eliminated by an ad hoc definition of this operator (which is the analogue of the introduction of normal products in conventional quantum field theory), and the same applies to the operator $\int \delta(q + q')D_{qq'}$. For the discussion of all these points, the reader is referred to Reference 9c. Equations of the type 39 have been considered, in another context, by E. Caianiello, Nuovo Cimento, 13, 637 (1959), under the name of "branching equations."

The linear functional Equation 40 will be the starting point of our discussion. It says that if the theory is renormalizable (as in the case under consideration), we should be able to find a set of renormalization constants such that there exists a Fréchet-Volterra type of solution. Our ignorance about existence theorems for linear equations, including functional differentiations, compels us to look for a method of solutions; we are therefore led to consider perturbative expansions in terms of the coupling parameter g_{ob} and introduce the following (formal) series into Equation 40:

$$\mathscr{P}u[j\,|\,g_{ob}, \kappa_{ob}] = \sum \frac{g_{ob}^n}{n!}\,\mathscr{P}u_n[j\,|\,\kappa_{ob}], \qquad A = \sum \frac{g_{ob}^n}{n!} A_n, \ \cdots. \tag{41}$$

Noting that in the right-hand side of Equation 39 no explicit differentiation with respect to g_{ob} occurs, we generate in this way, the following recurrent set:

$$\mathscr{P}u_{n+1} = i\mathscr{A}[D]\mathscr{P}u_n + \sum_{\rho=1}^{n} \binom{n}{\rho}\Big[N_\rho + A_\rho \int j(q)D_q$$

$$+ B_\rho \int \delta(q + q')D_{qq'} + iC_\rho\mathscr{A}[D]\Big]\,\mathscr{P}u_{n-\rho}. \tag{42}$$

Its interpretation is now straightforward. In a renormalizable field theory, the divergent counterterms (that is, the ones entering in the summations of the right-hand side) can be chosen in such a way that they counterbalance the divergences introduced by the interaction-operator $i\mathscr{A}[D]$ acting on $\mathscr{P}u_n$. The interpretation through Feynman diagrams is also straightforward; it suffices to note that the action of the operator D_q on a graph with n external lines (that is, with n factors of the form $\int j(p)\Delta(p)$), replaces it by the set of graphs where one external line has been removed and replaced by an internal one $\Delta(q)$. It follows, for instance, that the operator $i\mathscr{A}[D]$ acting on a graph with n external lines replaces it by a set of graphs, each of them having n - 3 external lines but one vertex more.

In order to show how the cancellation of divergent parts occurs in Equation 42, we shall calculate the first three approximations of $\mathscr{P}u_n$. We note first of all that since $u_0[j\,|\,\kappa_{ob}]$ is a Fréchet-Volterra functional, we may postulate

$$\mathscr{P}u_0 = u_0[j\,|\,\kappa_{ob}]. \tag{43}$$

Taking now n = 0 in Equation 42, we have

$$\mathscr{P} u_1 = - \int \delta(q + q' + q')\Delta(q)\Delta(q')\Delta(q'')j(q)j(q')j(q'')u_0[j \,|\, \kappa_{ob}], \tag{44}$$

which again is a functional of Fréchet-Volterra type.

The third approximation is more interesting; the equation reads

$$\begin{aligned}\mathscr{P} u_2 = & \int \delta(q_1 + q_2 + q_3)\delta(q_4 + q_5 + q_6)\hat{j}(q_1) \cdots \hat{j}(q_6)u_0[j] \\ & + 9 \int \delta(q_1 + q_2 + q_3 + q_4)\Delta(q_3 + q_4)\hat{j}(q_1) \cdots \hat{j}(q_4)u_0[j] \\ & + 18 \int \delta(q_1 + q_2)\Delta(q_1 - k)\Delta(k)\hat{j}(q_1)\hat{j}(q_2)u_0[j] \\ & + 6 \int \delta(q_1 + q_2 + q_3)\delta(q_1 + q_2 + q_3)\Delta(q_1)\Delta(q_2)\Delta(q_3)u_0[j] \\ & + N_1 + (2\Pi)^4 A_1 \int \delta(q_1 + q_2)\hat{j}(q_1)(q_1^2 + \kappa_{ob})\hat{j}(q_2) \\ & + B_1 \int \delta(q_1 + q_2)\hat{j}(q_1)\hat{j}(q_2) \\ & + C_1 \int \delta(q_1 + q_2 + q_3)\hat{j}(q_1)\hat{j}(q_2)\hat{j}(q_3)u_0[j/\kappa_{ob}],\end{aligned} \tag{45}$$

where

$$\hat{j}(p) = \int j(p)\Delta(p). \tag{46}$$

The two first integrals correspond to the second-order radiative corrections to, respectively, a diagram with six external lines (two disconnected vertices) and a diagram with four external lines (Möller scattering). The third one corresponds to a second-order proper self-energy part, and the fourth is a vacuum-to-vacuum diagram. They all result from the application of the operator $i\mathscr{A}[D]$ to $\mathscr{P}u_1$. Consider now the counterterms, that is, the four last integrals. Let us begin with the term $C_1 \int \cdots$. It is known that the $(g\Phi^3)$-theory has only even (odd) radiative corrections for propagators with even (odd) external lines. We postulate the same symmetry property to hold for the renormalized theory:

$$C_1 = 0. \tag{47}$$

The $A_1 \int \cdots$ and B_1 combine together, and, as we know, cancel the divergent part of the third integral of $\mathscr{P}u_2$. One may write, adding these three integrals,

$$\int \hat{j}(q_1)\delta(q_1 + q_2)[18\Delta(q_1 - k)\Delta(k) + (2\pi)^4 A_1(q_1^2 + \kappa_{ob}) + B_1]\hat{j}(q_2)$$

$$\equiv \int \hat{j}(q_1)\delta(q_1 + q_2)[\Pi^{*(2)}(q_1^2) + (2\pi)^4 A_1(q_1^2 + \kappa_{ob}) + B_1]\hat{j}(q_2)$$

$$\equiv \int \hat{j}(q_1)\delta(q_1 + q_2)\Pi_f^{*(2)}(q_1)\hat{j}(q_2). \tag{48}$$

Then

$$B_1 = \Pi^{*(2)}(-\kappa_{ob}) \qquad (2\pi)^4 A_1 = \left.\frac{\partial \Pi^{*(2)}}{\partial q_1^2}\right|_{q_1^2+\kappa_{ob}=0} \tag{49}$$

These equations are related to the analytical property of the two-point renormalized propagator that has a first-order pole on the mass shell. Finally, the last renormalization constant N_1 cancels the fourth integral of $\mathscr{P}u_2$:

$$6\int \delta(q_1 + q_2 + q_3)\delta(q_1 + q_2 + q_3)\Delta(q_1)\Delta(q_2)\Delta(q_3) + N_1 = 0. \tag{50}$$

In principle, the former method allows the calculations of all radiative corrections of higher order. The third-order radiative correction introduces 6 renormalized diagrams; the fourth-order, 17 renormalized diagrams; the fifth order, 37, and so on.

But all these radiative corrections require the consideration of a far greater number of diagrams which reduces to the given figures after cancellation, through the renormalization constants, of their divergent parts. For actual computations, simplifications are therefore welcomed. One may, for instance, try to express $\mathscr{P}u_n$ in terms of only connected diagrams. We do not want to enter into these technicalities; the interested reader will find all the details for the evaluation of $\mathscr{P}u_n$ for $n \leq 6$ in a forthcoming paper [7].

Let us conclude this section with a last remark. We have not explicitly introduced the regularization of the divergent integrals. As a matter of fact, for their explicit evaluation we do not need it, since, as in Equation 48, through the introduction of correctly chosen counterterms, we are always dealing with convergent integrals. The integral 48 taken as a whole is a convergent one. Condition 47 and the considerations following expression 49 about the analytical properties of a two-point propagator represent the price we are paying for such a simplification. It is interesting to make a few comments on this point for the three-point propagator. It is known that for a $g\Phi^3$ theory the second-order radiative correction of the vertex is given by a convergent integral. Thus if renormalization is intended as a method for the elimination of divergent results, one may conclude that no charge renormalization is needed. On the other hand, one may demand that the renormalized vertex reduces to 1 when two of its external momenta are on the mass shell. All of its radiative corrections should then vanish. This leads to a finite second-order renormalization. We chose this alternative in our numerical computations in order to meet an important feature of the vertex in quantum electrodynamics.

3. Quantum Electrodynamics[9]

Formally speaking, quantum electrodynamics has several features in common with $g\Phi^3$ theory. The important difference lies in the fact that besides the vector electromagnetic field $A_\mu(x)$ that requires the sources $J_\mu(x)$, we have the spinor fields $\psi(x)$, $\overline{\psi}(x)$ that require the spinor sources $\eta(x)$ and $\overline{\eta}(x)$. Furthermore, because of Fermi-Dirac statistics, the spinor sources should anticommute; they are no longer as in the scalar case (or even as the J_μ's) c-numbers but elements of a Grassman algebra.

The generating functional for the free field takes then the form

[9]See Reference 9c.

$$u_0[\eta, \bar{\eta}, J \mid m, \kappa] = \exp\left\{ -\frac{1}{2} \int \bar{\eta}_\alpha(x) S_{\alpha\beta}(x - x', m) \eta_\beta(x') - \frac{1}{4} \int J_\mu(x) \Delta(x - x', \kappa) J_\mu(x') \right\},$$

where S and Δ are the causal functions for the Dirac and vector field (we note that one avoids infrared divergences by giving the photon a mass $\sqrt{\kappa}$). The interaction operator is then

$$\exp\{ie\mathscr{A}[D]\} \equiv \exp\left\{ie \int d\xi\, \Gamma(\xi)\right\}$$

$$\Gamma(\xi) = \frac{\delta}{\delta\eta_\alpha(\xi)} \gamma^\mu_{\alpha\beta} \frac{\delta}{\delta\bar{\eta}_\beta(\xi)} \frac{\delta}{\delta J_\mu(\xi)},$$

and the generating functional of propagators for quantum electrodynamics takes the form

$$u[\eta, \bar{\eta}, J \mid m, \kappa] = \exp\left\{ie \int d\xi\, \Gamma(\xi)\right\} u_0[\eta, \bar{\eta}, J \mid m, \kappa].$$

The renormalized generating functional needs the introduction of 6 renormalization constants, $\mathscr{N}$, Z_1, Z_2, Z_3, δm, and $\delta\kappa$, which have to be chosen in such a way that

$$\mathscr{P}u[\eta, \bar{\eta}, J \mid e, m, \kappa] \equiv \frac{1}{\mathscr{N}} u\left[Z_2^{-1/2}\eta, Z_2^{-1/2}\bar{\eta}, Z_3^{-1/2}J \mid e_0, m - \delta m, \kappa - \delta\kappa\right],$$

with

$$Z_2 Z_3^{\frac{1}{2}} e_0 = Z_1 e,$$

is a Fréchet-Volterra functional. Gauge invariance of the renormalized theory requires

$$Z_1 = Z_2.$$

Once this step is reached, as in Equation 39, one forms the derivative $d\mathscr{P}u/de$ that is given by a linear integrodifferential operator acting on $\mathscr{P}u$. One then follows the same line of reasoning as in Section 2, in order to get a set of recurrent equations in $\mathscr{P}u_n$ analogous to the one obtained in Equation 42. This new set contains some extra terms because of the presence of spinor sources, but one deals in principle in the same way as we dealt with Equation 42. We obtain an algebraization of the well-known Salam's rule [5] for removing divergences in quantum electrodynamics. This same set of recurrent equations provides us with a powerful tool for the numerical evaluation of higher radiative corrections. These computations are not been yet completed but are in progress. Once again, due to the lack of space, we cannot enter into technical details but we refer the reader to the References 9c.

4. Conclusion

Through an analysis of the conventional renormalization theory, we have been able to organize the renormalized perturbation expansion of a renormalizable field theory and set up a computational method of renormalized higher radiative corrrections.

On the other hand, the convergence of the pertubative expansion has not been investigated, and the proof of the well-known criterion of renormalizability from the Lagrangian is, for the time being, an open question in our formulation.

References

1. The main ideas of the functional formulation and its applications to quantum electrodynamics are due to
   (a) J. Schwinger, Proc. Natl. Acad. Sci. U.S., 37, 452, 455 (1951).
   The generating functional of propagators has been studied by
   (b) K. Symanzik, Z. Naturforsch., 9, 809 (1964).
   (c) H. Lehman, K. Symanzik, and W. Zimmerman, Nuovo Cimento, 1, 1425 (1955) (see especially the Appendix).
   (d) H. Umezawa and A. Visconti, Nuovo Cimento, 1, 1079 (1955).
   For the relations between the generating functional and the $\mathscr{S}$ operator, the reader may be also referred to
   (e) K. Symanzik, J. Math. Phys., 1, 249 (1960).
   (f) A. Visconti and J. Carmona, Nuovo Cimento, 29, 742 (1963).
2. Donsker, M. B., and J. L. Lions, Acta Math., 108, 148 (1962
3. Dyson, F. J., Phys. Rev., 75, 1736 (1949).
4. Pauli, W., and F. Villars, Rev. Mod. Phys., 21, 434 (1949).

5. Salam, A., Phys. Rev., 82, 226 (1951).

6. Schwartz, L., Théorie des distributions, Hermann et Cie, Paris (1957), Vol. I, p. 38.

7. Soffer, J., and A. Visconti, to be published.

8. Visconti, A., et H. Umezawa, Compt. Rend., 252, 1910 (1961), and a paper by A. Visconti, Y. Le Gaillard, and J. Soffer, to be published.

9. (a) Visconti, A., and Y. Le Gaillard, Nuovo Cimento, 34, (1964).
   (b) Soffer, J., and A. Visconti, Nuovo Cimento, 38, 917 (1965).
   (c) Le Gaillard, Y., and A. Visconti, J. Math. Phys., 6, 1774 (1965).

10. Wightman, A. S., Proc. Int. Congr., Amsterdam (1962), p. 587.

Chapter 13

REMARKS ON THE PRESENT STATE OF AFFAIRS IN THE QUANTUM THEORY OF ELEMENTARY PARTICLES

A. S. Wightman

The organizing committee has asked me to open the meeting by giving a bird's-eye view of the current state of our subject. Since a systematic survey is neither possible nor desirable in the circumstances, what I offer is a series of remarks on various aspects of the current scene, related only by personal convictions, first, that there is an underlying unity in the apparent diversity of current approaches to theories, and, second, that we may be on the threshold of real progress in quantitative dynamics.

1. Is Relativistic Quantum Mechanics Adequate?

In the end the goal to which all the work discussed is directed is a quantitative theory of elementary particles. One wants to predict all those bumps in the probability distributions describing collisions of particles. The natural language to depict these phenomena appears to be relativistic quantum mechanics or in more specific form relativistic quantum field theory.

One of the characteristic frustrations of theoretical physics in the last 30 years is that it has been impossible to establish a single nontrivial theory consistent with the general principles of causality, relativistic invariance, etc., while at the same time every "radical" effort that abandoned such principles has experienced the customary fate of theories suffering from a lack of ideas: oblivion. Quantum field theory has turned out to be very robust. Its internal inconsistency was obvious in 1935; it is quite unobvious in 1965. Nevertheless, it has up to now successfully resisted all attempts at real mathematical control of its structure.

As always in a situation in which one does not know the physical laws involved, it is a matter of opinion whether an attempt to make a revolution or hard work along existing lines will be more fruitful. If relativistic quantum mechanics should turn out to be an inadequate language for the description of elementary particles, it would clearly be revolutionary. However, it is an elusive problem, unless it is examined in the context of specific theories.[1] Two approaches suggest themselves.

a. Refine, simplify, purify the part of the theory which starts from general principles and leads to detailed theories. This may give a clearer insight into what is essential for the working of the theory and may suggest fruitful generalizations or alternatives. I think the algebraic approach to local quantum theory which I will discuss shortly is an important example of this.
b. Try to work out the details of specific theories far enough so that their internal consistency is manifest or real paradoxes arise. This approach will be illustrated in the following by recent progress in the problem of proving that a quartically self-coupled Bose field exists.

Is relativistic quantum mechanics adequate for the description of elementary particles? We don't know, but none of the work that will be discussed has given any evidence of its inadequacy.

2. Algebraic Approach to Quantum Theory

I should like first to recall some of the ways that algebra gets into relativistic quantum theory and then to comment on recent related developments.

One way goes back to the very first papers on quantum mechanics. There the canonical commutation relations between the coordinate and momentum

$$[q, p]_- = i\hbar$$

were used to characterize the kinematics of the system while the dynamics was determined by giving the Hamiltonian as a function of q's and p's. For systems of a finite number of degrees of freedom, this point of view was put on a sound footing by von Neumann, who showed that under appropriate assumptions the canonical commutation relations have only one irreducible representation by Hermitian operators in a Hilbert space.

[1]In the circumstances, it is natural to turn to experiment to test the fundamental ideas of the theory. As an example, the proposal of M. Roos [25] to test the principle of superposition in high-energy collisions should be mentioned. Such tests are obviously worth while. However, just because they are of such great generality, unless their results come out negative, they are unlikely to provide much guidance in the development of elementary particle theory.

It took quite a long time before it was realized that for systems of an infinite number of degrees of freedom the analogous theorem is false; there are many inequivalent representations of the commutation relations. Thus the algebra of the commutation relations does not specify the kinematics in the sense that it does for systems of a finite number of degrees of freedom, because one has a choice of inequivalent representations. Furthermore, it turned out that not every representation of the canonical variables will make a given Hamiltonian mathematically meaningful. Thus the kinematics of systems of a infinite number of degrees of freedom is intimately connected with their dynamics. The most striking result supporting this statement is due to H. Araki, who showed that under certain assumptions the matrix elements of the Hamiltonian in a dense set of states are determined by the representation of the commutation relations; two different Hamiltonians require two different representations [3].

It is natural in these circumstances to think of trying to classify the representations of the commutation relations in order to provide labels for the possible dynamics. It turns out unfortunately that the commutation relations have too many representations to be classified with presently known techniques (In the terminology of Mackey [22] they are not type I.) Thus this program has progressed very slowly. However, there have been recent developments, some of which I should like to mention.

First, there is the work of Klauder, McKenna, and Woods [20]. They took up the idea launched by van Hove that representations of the commutation relations can be constructed in the infinite product spaces of von Neumann and brought it to a very satisfactory conclusion. They showed that in each of the so-called incomplete tensor products of which the tensor product is the direct sum there is an irreducible representation and these representations are unitarily equivalent if and only if the corresponding incomplete tensor products are weakly equivalent in the sense of von Neumann. Since von Neumann showed that weak equivalence can be characterized by the convergence or divergence of a certain numerical infinite product, this gives a very handy characterization of a large class of representations. It is interesting that certain fairly large groups of pseudocanonical transformations map this class of representations onto themselves and the above-mentioned numerical infinite product gives a neat criterion when such a pseudocanonical transformation is actually canonical, i.e., unitarily implementable. The Euclidean group provides a group of pseudocanonical transformations which so far has not been controlled in the setup of Klauder, McKenna, and Woods. It would be very interesting both theoretically and practically to do this and/or to obtain other classes of representations invariant under this group.

A second line of development which provides just such classes of representations occurs in the theory of the thermodynamic limit in statistical mechanics. (That is the limit as the number of particles in a system approaches infinity, the density being held fixed.) This limit has been shown to exist for a wide class of systems [15], and a beginning has been made on analyzing the nature of the representation obtained [6].

There is an important property which ought to be of considerable mathematical significance,[2] and which all the systems occurring in statistical mechanics have in common. The property is this. Consider the representation of the commutation relations obtained from the given one by restricting the support of the test functions to a bounded region. Then this representation ought to be quasi-equivalent in the sense of Mackey to the Fock representation. It is a striking fact pointed out by Federbush that nontrivial relativistic quantum field theories may be expected not to have this property [13].[3] Perhaps this is an example of the kind of distinction that in the end will make possible a useful classification of the inequivalent representations of the commutation relations.

There is another algebraic structure in relativistic quantum mechanics which, like that associated with the commutation relations, goes back many years. It is a realization of the idea that one should try to associate an algebraic structure with the set of all quantum mechanical observables. The pioneering work was done by Jordan, Wigner, von Neumann, and Segal. In the form which Segal gave the ideas the crucial notion is that quantum mechanical observables ought to be the self-adjoint elements of a C* algebra. States are defined as positive linear functionals on the algebra. At the previous conference Kastler and Haag reported on their work on this subject [17]. In my opinion there are at least three important new ideas in what they have done.

1. A new definition of physical equivalence of theories.
2. The introduction and systematic use of the structure associated with the local nature of measurements.[4]
3. The description of superselection rules in terms of inequivalent irreducible representations.

---

[2]The property is implicit in the treatment of various models. See, for example, R. Haag [16]. It has only very recently begun to be generally exploited. See G. F. Dell'Antonio, S. Doplicher, and D. Ruelle [10].

[3]What Federbush proves is that the expectation value of the bare particle number density operator in the physical vacuum may be expected to be infinite. It remains to be shown that no number operator exists.

[4]Of course, this development for C* algebras had been adumbrated by corresponding work in field theory and W* algebras.

About the first idea there is little to say. I do not know anyone who could disagree with it once he had heard it. It is somewhat revealing of the depth to which the fundamentals of quantum mechanics have been explored that a very much more restrictive definition was used for thirty years without question.

It is really very impressive how much content there is in the structure associated with the second idea. For a detailed account I recommend a forthcoming book by Araki in which collision theory is systematically developed from it [5]. As Kastler and Haag explain, the reason for this richness is not hard to find; most measurements are directly geometrical.

Until the third idea was proposed, there was only one rational description of superselection rules: as consequences of unobservable gauge groups. The idea here is that a theory is obtained by taking that particular representation of the underlying C* algebra of observables which is a direct sum of all irreducible physically acceptable representations. By general physical arguments the constituent irreducibles have to be unitarily inequivalent but physically equivalent. The content of the superselection rules of the theory is then the statement that the states which can be prepared in the laboratory are always direct sums of states on the constituent irreducibles.

It is clear that some real problems exist in connection with the adjective "physically acceptable." As an example, consider the following. It is generally admitted that the spectral condition on the energy momentum spectrum of a theory is essential in order to obtain a sensible account of macroscopic measurements. But that requirement was posed in the framework of the old definition of physical equivalence and there one could <u>prove</u> that the automorphisms of observables induced by translations were implemented by unitary transformations forming a continuous unitary representation of the translation group. In the present framework the translations are in general represented only by a set of automorphisms. What is meant by energy momentum spectrum in that case? Here definite progress has been made during the past year. Doplicher has given an algebraic condition which guarantees that the quasi-local algebra possess a representation which is an old-fashioned theory with continuous unitary representation satisfying the spectral condition and in fact having a unique vacuum state [11]. Borchers has shown that every other representation of this kind (with or without vacuum state) is locally unitarily equivalent to this one [8]. I won't go any further into this because there appear to be troubles in the published proofs. (One has to be prepared to risk chilblains in the arctic wastes of C* algebra theory in order to contribute to this subject.) Suffice it to say that it is likely that some further physical requirements will have to be imposed before one can decide the ultimate fate of this theory of superselection rules.

The previous discussion has been primarily about C* algebras generated by observables. One can also consider the corresponding von Neumann algebras. During this past year Araki brought his study of the von Neumann algebras associated with a neutral scalar boson field to a certain conclusion by showing that they are all factors of type I_∞ or III [4]. He separates the two cases by a simple criterion, and the theory yields a large supply of type III factors. Whether this is of interest to the professional students of von Neumann algebras will depend on the ease with which isomorphism or nonisomorphism of the examples can be established. So far there are no results.

During the past year there have been many studies of symmetry and broken symmetry within the C* or von Neumann algebra formalism. They take as definition of symmetry: mapping of the algebras on themselves preserving the C* algebra structure. My only remark about this is negative. One should not let the elegance and naturalness of this definition blind one to other possible meanings for the term which could be of much greater physical significance.

My last example of the intrusion of algebra into relativistic quantum theory illustrates this point and also has the exhilarating feature that it seems to have something directly to do with the real world. That is, the so-called algebra of currents used in the description of weak and strong interactions. The idea goes roughly as follows [14]. One assumes that in the description of strong interactions there is a finite set of currents $j_\mu^{(i)}(x)$ labeled by an index i, some conserved,

$$\partial^\mu j_\mu^{(i)}(x) = 0,$$

some perhaps not. Associated with these currents are quantities

$$Q_i(t) = \int_{x^0=t} d^3x j_0^{(i)}(x)$$

that have the commutation relations of a Lie algebra

$$[Q_i(t), Q_j(t)]_- = \sum_k c_{ij}^k Q_k(t), \qquad (1)$$

where the structure constants c_{ij}^k are independent of time. The occurrence of such a Lie algebra naturally leads to the idea that the corresponding simply connected Lie group will play a role in the dynamics. How does this come about? To answer this question it is helpful to recall how the Heisenberg commutation relations for a single particle

$$[q_j, p_k] = i\hbar\delta_{jk}, \qquad j, k = 1, 2, 3,$$

can be used to derive the dipole sum rule of the theory of atomic spectra. Let

$$H = \frac{\vec{p}^2}{2m} + V(\vec{q})$$

have a simple discrete spectrum with proper values E_i, proper functions Φ_i, $i = 1, 2, \cdots$:

$$H\Phi_i = E_i\Phi_i$$

(an assumption made for simplicity's sake, alone). The commutation relations for $\vec{q}$ and $\vec{p}$ imply

$$(\Phi_j, [H, \vec{q}]\Phi_k) = (E_j - E_k)(\Phi_j, \vec{q}\Phi_k) = \frac{\hbar}{2mi}(\Phi_j, \vec{p}\Phi_k).$$

Now, taking the expectation value of the commutation relation for $\vec{p}$ and $\vec{q}$ in the state Φ_j, one has

$$\sum_{\ell=1}^{3} (\Phi_j, (q_\ell p_\ell - p_\ell q_\ell)\Phi_j) = 3i\hbar,$$

which is, since the proper functions Φ_k are assumed to be a complete set,

$$\sum_{k=1}^{\infty}\sum_{\ell=1}^{3} (\Phi_j, q_\ell\Phi_k)(\Phi_k, p_\ell\Phi_j) - (\Phi_j, p_\ell\Phi_k)(\Phi_k, q_\ell\Phi_j) = 3i\hbar$$

This in turn is rewritten

$$\sum_{k=1}^{\infty}\left[\sum_{\ell=1}^{3} |(\Phi_j, q_\ell\Phi_k)|^2\left(\frac{E_k - E_j}{\hbar}\right)\right] = \frac{3\hbar}{4m}$$

if the matrix element of p_ℓ is replaced by that of q_ℓ using the foregoing relation. The importance of this simple identity arises from the fact that the quantities [ ] occurring on the left-hand side are precisely those occurring in the transition probability of an atom from the state j to the state k with the emission of dipole radiation. I have gone into this elementary calculation because its plan is precisely that used in deriving several of the most interesting consequences of the current commutation relations. I am referring to the calculations of the ratio of axial vector to vector coupling constants in β decay [1] and to the sum rules for the cross sections in neutrino nucleon collisions [2].

There are further consequences of the current commutation relations when assumptions are made that connect the Lie algebra more closely with the dynamics of the system. For example, consider a theory in which the commutation relations of Equation 1 hold, and in it a finite collection $\{\Phi_k\}$ of states lying low in mass. Then

$$(\Phi_\ell, [q_j(t), q_k(t)]\Phi_m) = \sum_r c^r_{jk}(\Phi_\ell, q_r\Phi_m).$$

Suppose that in the sums

$$(\Phi_\ell, q_j(t)q_k(t)\Phi_m) = \sum_r (\Phi_\ell, q_j(t)\Phi_r)(\Phi_r, q_k(t)\Phi_m),$$

where Φ_r runs over a complete orthonormal set including the above-mentioned $\{\Phi_k\}$, it is a good approximation to neglect all but the $\{\Phi_k\}$. Then the matrices $(\Phi_k, q_j\Phi_{k'})$ form a finite dimensional representation of the Lie algebra. Decomposing it into irreducible representations and assuming that the corresponding multiplets tend to be grouped in mass, one gets an explanation of the multiplicities of the low-lying multiplets of elementary particles as the dimensions of irreducible representation of the Lie algebra [9, 21].

It should be emphasized that the Lie group to which the current algebra gives rise need not be a symmetry group of the Hamiltoni In fact, it is an important problem to determine the circumstance under which the dynamics of a quantum field theory will make the approximations already discussed good ones. The proposal of a serious attack on this kind of problem does not seem quite as premature as it used to in view of recent developments that will now be described.

3. Existence Theorems for Nontrivial Theories

It was remarked before that the whole of quantum field theory suffers from the rarity of examples over which there is any real mathematical control. The work about which I am going to speak now is an effort to improve this situation by a frontal attack on the ancient question of the existence of solutions for the traditional formal field theories. The problem has a long and complicated history which I won't review. At the moment there are several quite different approaches to existence theorems of which I will list only

a. History integrals
b. Segal's infinite-dimensional manifold construction
c. Taylor's fixed-point method
d. Direct Hilbert space approach with nonrelativistic cutoff.

The first approach was discussed by Symanzik at the previous conference, and a detailed report on his work up to last year is available [2]. Recent developments, described in Symanzik's paper are very promising and interesting. The second was described in general terms at the last conference, and some new work on it has been reported since [26]. As yet Taylor's work is available only in preprint form [28]. The present status of his work is described in the present volume by Segal.

The first complete achievement of the type we have in mind under the fourth approach is due to Nelson [23], but the model is not relativistic. I also ought to mention work by Kato [19] and an announcement by Prosser [24]. The particular example which I am going to discuss in the following is that of a quartically self-coupled neutral scalar meson field. The results are due to Jaffe and are reported on in detail in his chapter in this volume. Here I want to try to bring out some general features of the situation which are relevant for any case in which these methods are used.

The heuristic equation of motion which we are trying to solve is

$$(\Box + m^2)\phi(x) = \lambda\phi^3(x). \tag{2}$$

The first point I want to make is that the validity of such an equation in a very weak sense is all that is required to deduce all the physical consequences which field theory implies. The definition of ϕ^3 will involve some limiting process, say,

$$\phi^3(x) = \lim_{x_1,x_2,x_3 \to x} [\phi(x_1)\phi(x_2)\phi(x_3) - f(x_1 - x_2, x - x_3)\phi(x_3)], \tag{3}$$

where x_1, x_2, x_3 and x are separated by spacelike intervals, and f is some function analytic at the stated points but with a singularity at $x_1 = x_2$, $x_1 = x_3$, and $x_2 = x_3$. (The second term in Equation 3 is only illustrative of the type of counter term used.) Then Equation 2 is <u>defined</u> to mean

$$(\Box_x + m^2)(\Psi_0, \phi(y_1) \cdots \phi(y_k)\phi(x)\phi(y_{k+1}) \cdots \phi(y_n)\Psi_0)$$

$$= \lim_{x_1,x_2,x_3 \to x} [(\Psi_0, \phi(y_1) \cdots \phi(y_k)\phi(x_1)\phi(x_2)\phi(x_3)\phi(y_{k+1}) \cdots \phi(y_n)\Psi_0)$$

$$- f(x_1 - x_2, x_1 - x_3)(\Psi_0, \phi(y_1) \cdots \phi(y_k)\phi(x_3)\phi(y_{k+1}) \cdots \phi(y_n)\Psi_0)]. \tag{4}$$

where all intervals between the points $y_1 \cdots y_k, x, y_{k+1} \cdots y_n$ and between the points $y_1 \cdots y_k, x_1, x_2, x_3, y_{k+1} \cdots y_n$ are space like. The general theory of fields assures us that for such arguments all the indicated vacuum expectation values are analytic except where one argument coincides with another. The question of the adequacy of such a definition is an existence problem: does there exist a field ϕ which satisfies Equation 4? The satisfactory character of this type of definition can be verified in a number of models; there are no grounds for suspecting its inadequacy. Evidently, if this point of view is accepted, a theory of renormalization is difficult to separate from a theory of existence of solutions That is what makes the theory of renormalization hard.

The proposed method is ancient. One expands the fields in a box with periodic boundary conditions and a cutoff

$$\phi_\kappa(\vec{x}) = \sum_k (\hat{\phi}(\vec{k})\, e^{i\vec{k}\cdot\vec{x}} + \hat{\phi}(\vec{k})^*\, e^{-i\vec{k}\cdot\vec{x}})\hat{\chi}_\kappa(\vec{k}),$$

$$\pi_\kappa(\vec{x}) = i \sum_\kappa (\hat{\phi}(\vec{k})\, e^{i\vec{k}\cdot\vec{x}} - \hat{\phi}(\vec{k})^*\, e^{-i\vec{k}\cdot\vec{x}})\hat{\chi}_\kappa(\vec{k}),$$

where $\hat{\chi}_\kappa$ is a cutoff function vanishing for $|\vec{k}| > \kappa$. One takes as Hamiltonian

$$H_\kappa = H_0 + \lambda \int_V : \phi_\kappa(\vec{x})^4 : d\vec{x},$$

where H_0 is the free-field Hamiltonian in a box. When one uses this cut-off Hamiltonian to give the time development of the field, one finds that the field satisfies

$$(\Box + m^2)\phi(\vec{x}, t) = -4\lambda \int_V : \phi_\kappa(\vec{y}, t)^3 : \chi_\kappa(\vec{y} - \vec{x})\, d\vec{y}, \tag{5}$$

where the equality is again understood in the very weak sense analogous to that described earlier. The vacuum expectation values and Green's functions (time-ordered vacuum expectation values) exist, and the latter satisfy

$$(\Box_{x_1} + m^2)\langle T[\phi(x_1) \cdots \phi(x_n)]\rangle_0$$

$$= -i \sum_{j=2}^{n} \delta(x_1 - x_j)\langle T[\phi(x_2) \cdots \phi(x_j) \cdots \phi(x_n)]\rangle_0$$

$$+ \langle T[J(x_1)\phi(x_2) \cdots \phi(x_n)]\rangle_0, \qquad (6)$$

where

$$J(\vec{x}, t) = -4\lambda \int_V dy_1 \cdots dy_4\, K(\vec{x}, \vec{y}_1 \cdots \vec{y}_4) : \phi(\vec{y}_1, t) \cdots \phi(\vec{y}_4, t) :$$

and

$$K(x, \vec{y}_1 \cdots \vec{y}_4) = \int d\vec{y} \prod_{j=1}^{4} \chi_\kappa(\vec{y} - \vec{y}_j)\chi_\kappa(\vec{y} - \vec{x}).$$

The idea is that the solution of Equation 2 is obtained from Equation 5 in the limit $V, \kappa \to \infty$.

The last set of equations, 6, can be reworked into a form

$$x = \mathsf{T}(x), \qquad (7)$$

where x is a vector whose components are a list of Green's functions (truncated, amputated in all but one variable, and supplemented by the list of their one-particle irreducible parts if necessary.) Here T is a nonlinear integral operator.

To study the solutions of this equation or its analogues by methods a and c, previous authors have made a variety of alterations in the theory, including some of the following:

1. Passage to Euclidean world
2. Ultraviolet cutoff
3. Space-Time Box
4. Amputation of higher Green's functions

If an existence theorem has been proved under the first assumption, it is a nontrivial problem to show that it implies the existence of a corresponding solution in Minkowski space. What I would like to point out is that (granting him his very violent cutoff) Jaffe has solved this problem. Furthermore, he has shown that there is no solution in Hilbert space for the $\lambda\phi^3$ theory and for the $\lambda\phi^4$ theory with the wrong sign of λ. I think there is very likely a moral in this. When you solve equations like Equation 7, it can happen that you get a solution in which probability is not conserved. One of the great virtues of the Hilbert space formalism is that this can't happen. If you get a solution at all, it will conserve probability. These remarks suggest a classification of methods of proving existence theorems in this kind of butchered quantum field theory: to be nontrivial a method must fail on the $\lambda\phi^3$ theory.

Of course, Jaffe's results leave the main question open: Is there a limit as the cutoff goes away? However, there are several general remarks that can be made even at this stage. First, of all, it is the vacuum expectation values and Green's functions which ought to converge, and nothing else. As Jaffe describes in his chapter, there are examples in which neither the ground state $\psi_{\kappa 0}$ nor the one-parameter group $e^{iH_\kappa t}$ converges, strongly or weakly. However, the vacuum expectation values and Green's functions of these simple examples do converge as tempered distributions. Second, if the vacuum expectation values of the cutoff $\lambda\phi^4$ theory converge as tempered distributions and the limit distributions are relativistically invariant, then they necessarily satisfy the spectral conditions and positive definiteness. Thus by the reconstruction theorem one can recover a Hilbert space, a continuous unitary representation of the Poincaré group, and a field which has just the limit distributions as vacuum expectation values. Third, it may very well be that by combining fixed point methods for Equation 7 with what has already been learned from the fourth approach one can get at the question of convergence.

Conclusion

I have reached the end of my biased survey without mentioning collision theory, axiomatic S-matrix theory, and various other interesting subjects. If I have done so it is not only for lack of time. It is because I think that many of the problems of collision theory and S-matrix theory would take on new life if viewed in the context of a dynamics whose existence was not in doubt. Now it seems that a solution to the existence problems may be within rea

References

1. Adler, S., Phys. Rev. Letters, 14, 1051 (1965).
Weissberger, W. A., Phys. Rev. Letters, 14, 1047 (1965).

2. Adler, S., Tests of Local Commutation Relations in High Energy Neutrino Reactions, CERN preprint.
3. Araki, H., J. Math. Phys., 1, 492 (1960).
4. Araki, H., Prog. Theoret. Phys., 32, 956 (1964).
5. Araki, H., Local Quantum Theory, W. A. Benjamin Inc., New York, 1966.
6. Araki, H., and E. J. Woods, J. Math. Phys., 4, 637 (1963).
7. Araki, H., and J. Wyss, Helv. Phys. Acta, 37, 136 (1964).
8. Borchers, H. A., Comm. Math. Phys., I, 57 (1965).
9. Dashen, R. G., and M. Gell-Mann, Phys. Letters (Amsterdam), 17, 142 (1965).
10. Dell' Antonio, G. F., S. Doplicher, and D. Ruelle, in Proceedings of the 1964 Cargèse Summer School, ed. M. Lévy, Gordon & Breach, New York, 1966.
11. Doplicher, S., Comm. Math. Phys., I, 1 (1965).
12. Ezawa, H., J. Math. Phys., 5, 1078 (1964); 6, 380 (1965).
13. Federbush, P., Nuovo Cimento, 15, 932 (1960).
14. Gell-Mann, M., Physics, I, 63 (1964), and earlier papers quoted there.
15. Ginibre, J., J. Math. Phys., 6, 238 (1964), and references quoted there.
16. Haag, R., Nuovo Cimento, 25, 287 (1962).
17. Haag, R., and D. Kastler, J. Math. Phys., 5, 848 (1964).
18. Kastler, D., and R. Haag, in Analysis in Function Space, pp. 179-196.
19. Kato, Y., Prog. Theoret. Phys., 26, 99 (1961).
20. Klauder, J. R., J. McKenna, and E. J. Woods, Direct Product Representations of the Canonical Commutation Relations, preprint.
21. Lee, B. W., Phys. Rev. Letters, 14, 673, 850 (1965).
22. Mackey, G. W., Bull. Amer. Math. Soc., 69, 628 (1963).
23. Nelson, E., J. Math. Phys., 5, 190 (1964).
24. Prosser, R. T., Bull. Amer. Math. Soc., 69, 552 (1963).
25. Roos, M., J. Math. Phys., 5, 1609 (1964).
26. Segal, I. E., in Analysis in Function Space, p. 129; Jour. de Math. Pures et Appliquées, 44, 71, 107 (1965).

27. Symanzik, K., in Analysis in Function Space, p. 197; A Modified Model of Euclidean Quantum Field Theory, N.Y.U. Courant Institute IMM-NYU 327, June 1964.

28. Taylor, J. G., On the Existence of Field Theory, I, II.

PROGRAM OF SCHEDULED SCIENTIFIC EVENTS

September 12, Sunday	
Evening	Opening Address: Remarks on the Present of Affairs in the Quantum Theory of Elementary Particles, Arthur S. Wightman
September 13, Monday	
Morning	On the Calculation of Some Holomorphy Envelopes of Interest in Physics, Gunnar Källén
	Existence Theorems for a Cut-Off $\lambda\phi^4$ Field Theory, Arthur Jaffe
	Recent Applications of Topology to the Analytic Properties of Scattering Amplitudes, Marcel Froissart
Afternoon	Symmetry Groups and Elementary Particles, Louis Michel
	Spontaneous Breakdown of Symmetry, R. F. Streater
	The Attempts To Combine Space-Time and Internal Symmetries, Sidney Coleman
	Norm-Invariance of Maxwell's Equations Under the Conformal Group, Leonard Gross
September 14, Tuesday	
Morning	A Two-Dimensional Model in Quantum Field Theory, Edward Nelson
	Remarks on Functional Integration, David Shale
	Infraparticle Structure and Functional Integrals, Jan Tarski
	A New Method for Euclidean Quantum Field Theory, Kurt Symanzik

Afternoon

Asymptotic Behavior of Solutions of Nonlinear Partial Differential Equations, Irving Segal

Twisted Convolutions and C* Algebras of a Free Boson Field, Daniel Kastler

Twisted Convolution Algebras, John Lewis

September 15, Wednesday

Morning

Parafield Theory, O. W. Greenberg

A Proof of the Mandelstam Hypothesis, Roland Omnes

Fixed-Point Methods in Quantum Field Theory, John Taylor

Discussion: Symmetry Principles, Louis Michel, Leader.

Afternoon

A Field-Theory-Like Axiom System, David Ruelle

On the Structure of the Finite Parts in Renormalizable Quantum Field Theories, Antoine Visconti

Discussion: Axiomatic Field Theory, Rudolf Haag, Leader.

LIST OF PARTICIPANTS

Conference on Mathematical Theory of Elementary Particles

Major B. R. AGINS	Air Force Office of Scientific Research,
Huzihiro ARAKI	Kyoto University, Japan
Sidney COLEMAN	Harvard University
Stanley DESER	Brandeis University
Henri EPSTEIN	Centre National de la Recherche Scientifique, Paris
Paul FEDERBUSH	Massachusetts Institute of Technology
Jacob FELDMAN	University of California, Berkeley
J. M. G. FELL	University of Pennsylvania
Marcel FROISSART	Institute for Theoretical Physics, Orsay, S. et O., France
Roy J. GLAUBER	Harvard University
Roe GOODMAN	Massachusetts Institute of Technology
O. W. GREENBERG	University of Maryland
Leonard GROSS	Cornell University
Rudolph HAAG	University of Illinois
Klaus HEPP	Eidgenossische Technische Hochschule, Zürich, Switzerland
Arthur JAFFE	Princeton University
Kenneth JOHNSON	Massachusetts Institute of Technology
John J. JONES, Jr.	Air Force Office of Scientific Research
Res JOST	Eidgenossische Technische Hochschule, Zürich, Switzerland
Mark KAC	Rockefeller University, New York
Gunnar KÄLLÉN	University of Lund, Sweden

Daniel KASTLER	University of Marseille, France
Jean LASCOUX	Centre de Physique Théorique, Paris, France
Benjamin W. LEE	University of Pennsylvania
John LEWIS	Oxford University, England
George W. MACKEY	Harvard University
Paul C. MARTIN	Harvard University
Louis MICHEL	Institut des Hautes Études Scientifiques, France
Edward NELSON	Princeton University
Roland OMNES	Centre de Recherches Nucléaires, Strasbourg-Cronenbourg, France
R. S. PALAIS	Brandeis University
Robert G. POHRER	Air Force Office of Scientific Research
Reese PROSSER	Lincoln Laboratory, Massachusetts Institute of Technology
Arlan RAMSAY	University of Rochester
Paul ROMAN	Boston University
David RUELLE	Institut des Hautes Études Scientifiques, France
Silvan S. SCHWEBER	Brandeis University
Irving SEGAL	Massachusetts Institute of Technology
David SHALE	University of Pennsylvania
Donn SHANKLAND	Wright-Patterson Air Force Base, Ohio
I. M. SINGER	Massachusetts Institute of Technology
Stephen SMALE	University of California, Berkeley
Schlomo STERNBERG	Harvard University
Raymond F. STREATER	Imperial College, London, England
Kurt SYMANZIK	New York University
Jan TARSKI	Columbia University
René THOM	Institut des Hautes Études Scientifiques, France